PHOTOGRAPHY
FOR SCIENTIFIC PUBLICATION

A SERIES OF BOOKS IN BIOLOGY

Weevil ($\times$45).

[SPECIMEN PROVIDED BY BARBARA BARR.]

Lighting is with one direct spotlight from the upper left, with a white card reflector at lower right. Great care is needed here to light so as to provide a good impression of roundness and modeling while preserving good shadow detail.

PHOTOGRAPHY
FOR SCIENTIFIC PUBLICATION

A Handbook

ALFRED A. BLAKER

Principal Photographer, Scientific Photographic Laboratory, University of California, Berkeley

 W. H. FREEMAN AND COMPANY *San Francisco and London*

© *Copyright 1965 by W. H. Freeman and Company*

The publisher reserves all rights to reproduce this book in whole or in part, with the exception of the right to use short quotations for review of the book.

Library of Congress Catalog Card Number 65-13569

Printed in the United States of America

4 5 6 7 8 9

ACKNOWLEDGEMENTS

A handbook such as this is necessarily a synthesis rather than a work of great originality. The author of such a book must read, observe, be taught—and then adapt widely and freely. In a very real sense such a book is the sum of the experience of a great many people, not all of whom can be identified. But some direct help can be clearly recognized, and those who gave it can be given the deserved credit.

Without the five years of excellent on-the-job training at the Scientific Photographic Laboratory under Victor G. Duran, my working superior during that period and—prior to his retirement—my predecessor in my present position, I could never have undertaken this work.

Nor could the great variety of specifically oriented illustrations in this handbook have been collected without the kind cooperation of certain people who have had work done at the Laboratory, and who have allowed me to use the photographs here. These people are identified in the captions of the various plates, and their credits are somewhat amplified in the introduction to the plates.

It is appropriate here also to express my thanks to my wife and children for their patience during a time of unusual neglect, and grateful thanks to Dr. Ralph Emerson and Mr. John D. Arms for reading the manuscript and offering much helpful criticism.

Last, but perhaps most, I must give credit to Dr. E. S. Evans, Chairman of the University of California Scientific Photographic Laboratory's guiding Faculty Committee, and the two other Committee members, Dr. Max Alfert and Dr. Robert D. Raabe, for encouraging the experimentation necessary to develop and refine many of the techniques described in this handbook.

There is no intent here to endorse the products of any business firm or manufacturer. Where particular products are mentioned by name, it is either as an example of a type or as a guide where the available types are few and the named item clearly tops the field. The author has no connection whatever with any of the firms mentioned.

Berkeley, California
December, 1964

ALFRED A. BLAKER

CONTENTS

LIST OF TEXT FIGURES

INTRODUCTION

This handbook is intended to provide a source of useful and practical information about photography for those persons who need to make pictures to illustrate articles to be submitted for scientific publication. Lacking access to a suitably staffed and equipped photographic production unit, many researchers must learn to do their own photography, but the available literature on the subject often leaves them without the particular knowledge they most need. Consequently, the quality of scientific illustrations, in journals and elsewhere, is often not consistent with that of the text they accompany. Because the clarity of an article or a monograph depends in part on the clarity of its illustrations, it seems desirable to do what one can to see that the presentation is not impaired by inadequate photographs.

Since scientific publication is somewhat limited in scope, this handbook is similarly limited. The main consideration is black-and-white still photography, of objects falling between infinity focus and magnifications of up to about ×60. The text emphasizes, but is not limited to, subject matter which is motionless or nearly so at the moment of exposure. There is supplementary material on color work, this section being informative but not extensive. Throughout, the approach is pragmatic, in terms of what one *needs* to know to accomplish the stated ends, rather than in terms of theory and ideal circumstances.

No attempt is made to cover areas considered already well covered elsewhere, except as it is necessary to furnish a summary to assure full understanding of a given situation. Standard photomicrography of microscope slides falls into that category. The same applies to techniques involving special equipment and attachments, such as photography of spectra, through telescopes, or of oscilloscope traces. Such highly specialized matters have already been either the subject of a book or covered sufficiently in specialized literature in the field. Discussion here concerns the demands—not inconsiderable in themselves—of generalized photographic practice as applied to specialized subject matter and situations. It centers about those things which can be photographed using normally available photographic equipment, lights, lenses, and supplies—without microscopes or other such paraphernalia—and requiring the application of broad photographic knowledge rather than narrow technical expertise for successful completion. It is in this area, I think, that the greatest lack of published material exists.

However limited the nature of the subject matter and the scope of the photography that a reader intends doing, I strongly suggest a careful reading of the entire text. This handbook is written primarily in terms of general principles. Particular applications and examples are widely discussed in the later sections, but their discussion will be in terms of the earlier text. Since the likely subject matter is so widely scattered in types, and since the reader's needs can not be predicted, it is both more practical and of greater service to proceed in this manner. The very unpredictability of the reader's needs may make a seemingly unrelated piece of information just what he needs to solve some new problem.

The general pattern of presentation is to divide photographic practice into its various major components, and then take each component and give a general background, a technical résumé, and a discussion of its special problems. Part I is a skeleton survey of basic photography, followed by a discussion of general techniques (Part II) and a section (Part III) on the solutions to general problems and on particular applications. The emphasis is always on what, in practice, one needs to know in order to do work of publication quality. A bibliography is provided for those desiring or needing more information and deeper coverage on various subjects covered lightly or not covered at all here.

At times it may seem to the reader that there is too much or unnecessary emphasis on the idea of quality. But unless such emphasis is adhered to, there seems little need for this book at all. Anyone can do bad work. This handbook is intended and written for those who wish to improve, and from it one can draw such lessons as he feels the need for.

No claims are made to complete knowledge or to originality of techniques. The methods described here are those found useful in practice by me, my predecessors and associates, and other practitioners in the field.

PART

I

A Review of Essentials

In any work of this sort it is necessary to assume that the reader has already a working knowledge of fundamental photography; however, it is in no way out of line to provide a brief review of the essentials. And, paradoxically, in such a review it is safest to assume nothing, since there is no way of telling which elements are weak or missing in the knowledge of any individual reader.

1

BASIC PHOTOGRAPHY

Photography in practice consists of two rather mechanical operations and a relatively intuitive one. The former two are calculation of exposure, and the actual operation of the camera itself; the latter one is the whole combined operation of choosing, isolating, and lighting the subject. Since operating the camera is a simple matter of manual dexterity depending upon the make and model chosen and is provided for in the instruction manual accompanying the purchase, it will not be covered here. Choosing, isolating, and lighting the subject are major matters which will make up the main text of this handbook.

Calculation of Exposures

Calculation of correct exposures is dependent upon the interaction of three variables and upon maintaining a correct and useful relationship among them. These variables are (1) film speed, (2) diaphragm opening, and (3) exposure time. Under most circumstances exposure can readily be correctly determined within adequate limits by using a light meter and following the instruction book provided with it. But *intelligent* use requires just a little more.

The film speed is specified by the manufacturer and is a constant based upon the response of the given film to the action of light, when used under specified normal conditions. Generally, slow films are fine-grained and have relatively brilliant over-all tonal gradation, while fast films have larger grain structure and less contrast. (By "slow" and "fast" films we mean films requiring relatively longer or shorter exposures under given circumstances.) For most purposes in scientific illustration a slow film is to be preferred, and particularly if a small camera, requiring subsequent enlargement of the pictures, is being used.

Films are, in various countries, rated by different scales. Here we will use only the American Standard rating, usually called ASA. Scales of foreign equivalents are readily available. A film rated at ASA 25 or 50 would be considered slow; one rated at ASA 500 to 1600, fast. Films in intermediate categories are simply called medium-speed films.

Figure 1. *The law of reciprocity*

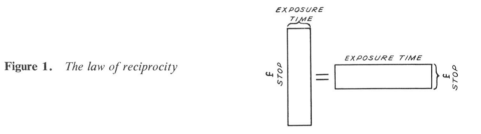

All calculations of exposure require a clear understanding of what is known as "the law of reciprocity." As a useful simplification it can briefly be summarized by saying that, using a given film, a long exposure with a small diaphragm opening is equivalent to a short exposure with a large opening, providing that the two exposures are balanced so that each passes to the film the same total amount of light. This simple formulation is diagramed in Figure 1.

The reciprocity law applies in all cases *except* where the exposure time is either extremely short or extremely long (for practical purposes, shorter than 1/1000 second or longer than 20 seconds with black-and-white films, or shorter than 1/1000 second or longer than ½ second with most color films). With either very short or very long exposure times the required correction is the same: relatively *more* exposure is needed than calculations indicate. In these cases the exposure is said to suffer from "reciprocity failure." If the particular nature of the work requires such short or long exposures, then tests of the film to be used should be made to determine how much compensatory exposure is required. Manufacturers can also be queried.

Functions of Diaphragm and Shutter

Reference to any adjustable camera will show that the amount of light reaching the film can be varied by opening or closing the iris diaphragm at the lens, or by changing the speed of the shutter. Present practice is to graduate the diaphragm scale as shown, and designate the shutter scale in one of the two following ways.

Table 1

Diaphragm Opening (f-number)	Shutter Speed (seconds)	
	System 1	System 2
1.4	1	1
2	1/2	1/2
2.8	1/5	1/4
4	1/10	1/8
5.6	1/25	1/15
8	1/50	1/30
11	1/100	1/60
16	1/200	1/125
22	1/400	1/250
32	1/800	1/500
45		1/1000
64		
90		

In all three columns the top figures pass the most light, and each succeeding one roughly halves the light passage of its predecessor.

The individual diaphragm graduations are generally called "f-stops," and the difference between any two graduations on *either* scale (either diaphragm or shutter, that is) a difference of one "stop."

By using a light meter which has been set for the speed of the film being used, one can measure the light available in a given situation and arrive, via the meter scale, at a variety of diaphragm-shutter speed combinations, any of which will provide correct exposure of the film. Then comes the matter of choosing a combination which will best fulfill the needs of the individual case.

Adjustment of the exposure time is, of course, the means by which action—if present—is "stopped"; fast shutter speeds "stop" motion better than slow speeds, of course. Thus, this time scale serves the double function of varying the amount of light reaching the film and controlling the degree to which action is stopped.

The diaphragm also serves a double function. It varies the amount of light reaching the film and, in addition, controls "depth of field," which is defined as that amount of fore-and-aft depth in the scene being photographed that is seen as acceptably "in focus" in the picture or on the ground glass of the camera. A wide opening of the diaphragm (such as f/2) provides shallow depth, while a small opening (such as f/64) gives much greater depth of field. Obviously a lens focused at a distance of 4 feet gives an image truly in focus only at that distance, and if the diaphragm is opened to f/2 or wider this is substantially the case, with only a very narrow band of space acceptably focused. But if the diaphragm is "stopped down" to f/22 the depth of the scene rendered acceptably sharp in the image will be quite extensive (from about 3 feet to about 5 feet, if the focus is at about 4 feet). Depth of field will be discussed at greater length in the later section on Magnifications.

Selection of Camera Settings

With the foregoing clearly in mind it is possible to arrive at a reasonable choice of shutter speed and diaphragm opening (or f-stop). It will depend upon the relative importance of the speed of the action to be stopped versus the depth of field desired. Motionless subjects allow depth to determine the choice. Subject matter or action in a single plane of focus allows speed to determine the choice. All other situations require compromise in one direction or the other. The situation as a whole therefore rules, subject to the whims and desires of the photographer. In cases where speed and depth are both involved, it will help to use a faster film if the intensity of the light illuminating the scene can not be increased. If this is done, however, the negative will have larger grain and less over-all contrast. Whether this is important depends upon the subject matter and the use to be made of the negative.

Films

Although there are a number of special films for special purposes it is fair to state that, generally, black-and-white films are divided into three groups:

PANCHROMATIC

Panchromatic films, which record the relative brightnesses of the various colors in a scene roughly as the eye does, are the most commonly used materials in the type of photography being discussed here. The approximate correspondence of panchromatic films to the sensitivity of the eye is exceptionally useful. It is possible to use filters to differentiate a wide range of colors from one another (in varying shades of gray, of course). It is also possible to determine roughly the effect of a filter simply by looking through it and observing the resulting changes in relative brightness of various subject areas.

ORTHOCHROMATIC

Orthochromatic films are sensitive to green, blue, and violet, but not to the reds. These films are useful where their sensitivity range accords with that of the subject matter or with the photographer's notion of what he wishes to record. Orthochromatic effects can usually be simulated by using suitable filters with panchromatic materials, but only at a great cost in film speed. Ortho films are very commonly used in copying.

NON-COLOR-SENSITIVE

Non-color-sensitive films record only in the blue-violet area. These films are no longer used for general photography, but are usually reserved for making transparencies or for other similarly limited uses.

In the following sections specialized discussions of matters covered above are provided as needed, and more detailed information can be had by reference to information sources listed in the Bibliography.

2

CHOICE OF EQUIPMENT

Cameras

In general photography for nonprofessional purposes, the choice of a camera to be used depends most strongly on the preferences and prejudices of the prospective buyer—whether he values most of all extreme mobility, or perhaps the ability to record infinite static detail. Generally the present-day casual photographer chooses the small, light camera for its ease of handling and air of inconspicuousness. The reasons given are usually excellent, and in knowledgeable hands some of these instruments are capable of fine photographs. There remain, however, a few hardy souls willing to use (and even backpack into the countryside) large view cameras, up to 8 × 10 inches in film size and occasionally larger. Again, the reasons for doing so are usually excellent, and if ably used these cameras can yield pictures of truly superb photographic quality.

In photography for scientific publication the choice of camera must also be dependent upon your preference, but—if purchase is still being contemplated or a change is being considered—you should look carefully at the requirements of the particular subject matter and the capabilities of the particular equipment before deciding. Although the techniques of photography to be discussed later are applicable in most cases to nearly any camera type, depending of course on the availability of accessories in some cases, it will be worth while to consider the nature of the types available.

SMALL CAMERAS, VIRTUES AND DEFECTS

For supreme mobility, for ease and speed of handling, for economy in film costs, and for ability to follow action, by far the best all-around choice is the high-quality small camera of 35 mm or $2\frac{1}{4}$-inch format. Quality of design and manufacture of both lens and body is essential for really good work, as the degree of enlargement for publication-sized prints is considerable, and any defects will soon make themselves visible. Fortunately, there are many good models to choose from, and several are really superb.

In the 35-mm field there are two types, rangefinder and single-lens reflex. With the first, one views through an optical viewfinder, which usually incorporates an optical rangefinder coupled with the focusing mount of the lens. Such cameras are very fast-handling and in the best makes are very good indeed. They are excellent for such uses as recording human activity, where the photographer must be inconspicuous and mobility is essential. One disadvantage is that they must be brought to the eye for accurate focusing. Another is that framing can never be entirely accurate because the viewfinder does not see exactly the same scene as the lens; it is slightly off the optical axis of the camera and is designed—for safety reasons, to avoid accidental exclusion of part of the subject—to include a little less area than the film actually records. These cameras are generally poor for close-up or high-magnification work. Attachments are often provided for these uses, but in practice they are usually inconvenient, unhandy, and expensive.

Single-lens reflex cameras come in a variety of sizes, from the large cut-film formats on down, but the vast majority are either of 35-mm size or, probably in smaller numbers, of the $2\frac{1}{4}$-inch square format on 120-size film. These two small sizes are generally similar in design and operation. (Those larger than $2\frac{1}{4}$ inches in format tend to be rather cumbersome. Although useful in some areas they will not be considered here, and the remarks following apply only to the smaller sizes.) In this type of camera viewing is accomplished through the taking lens by way of an internal mirror which moves out of the line of light at the moment of exposure. Nearly all the features of the rangefinder type are present, but the viewing system makes framing more accurate (in a few cases absolutely so) and renders close-up work both convenient and quite easy, as well as speedy. These cameras are especially well suited to close-up photography of living and moving organisms. For working inconspicuously these cameras are good, since some models allow the use of waist-level viewfinders. A disadvantage in this same area is that the focal-plane shutters usually used are often quite noisy compared to the leaf-type shutters used in rangefinder models. But single-lens reflex cameras commonly accept great varieties of lenses and accessories, and hence offer much versatility.

A popular type of camera for many years in the journalistic and documentary areas has been the twin-lens reflex, an instrument which is in effect two cameras, one mounted on top of the other. The top lens uses a mirror to provide viewing, from the top, of a good-sized ($2\frac{1}{4}$-inch square) ground glass image area, and the bottom lens does the actual picture taking. The two lenses are of similar types and are coupled so that they focus together. The better makes have automatic "parallax" correction, to compensate partially for the difference in viewing position of the two lenses. These cameras are excellent for ethnological recording and the like, but less so for other scientific work. They are particularly poor for close-up and magnification work. Accessories are limited, and interchangeability of lenses is either nonexistent or very limited.

All these cameras allow great economy in terms of film costs, particularly with color film. This is in part nullified by a general tendency to take advantage of the economy feature by making many exposures of the same subject to "make sure." Forethought and good training can help to obviate such waste, but in any event this economy feature is overrated. In all photography the cost of film is negligible compared to equipment and labor cost, except in those limited fields where truly enormous numbers of purely record pictures are needed.

A disadvantage of small film sizes in general is the necessity to enlarge in printing. Enlarging is often expensive in terms of both time and auxiliary equipment, and introduces a good chance of loss of quality, particularly since only the best—and most expensive—enlarger lenses are of sufficient quality for professional results. The necessity to enlarge also limits the speed of films which can be used if excessive grain is to be avoided.

LARGE CAMERAS, VIRTUES AND DEFECTS

The ultimate in picture quality is obtained when the negative is large enough to allow complete choice of films, contact printing, and such negative manipulation as may be desirable and permissible. With contact printing (printing in which the negative is in actual contact with the printing paper) the time required is somewhat shortened and there is no need to own an enlarger or to suffer quality loss through its misuse. And, in the actual picture taking, the composition, setup, and lighting are often simplified by the ability to see results on a large and clearly visible ground glass.

In this field there are two main types, the press camera and the view camera.

(Single-lens reflexes are also available in some large sizes, but are relatively uncommon.) Though smaller sizes are available, discussion here will be limited to cameras of film sizes of 4 × 5 inches or larger. Smaller cameras of these types offer few really significant advantages over the small cameras just covered.

The usual press camera consists essentially of a box body, with a front plate which folds down to become a support and track mechanism for the lens. The lens is coupled to an optical rangefinder. The back of the body-box carries a ground-glass viewing screen and an arrangement for insertion of various types of film holders (see Figure 2). For versatility in these larger

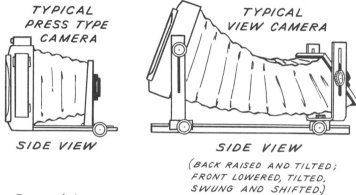

Figure 2. *Press and view cameras*

cameras, coupled with mobility, speed, and ease of handling, the 4 × 5 press camera is best. The negative is large enough to contact print for most scientific uses, and operation in the manner of the 35-mm rangefinder camera is practical and common. Additionally, since these cameras have a double- or triple-extension bellows and some view camera movements, they can be used fairly extensively as view cameras and can obtain good results in close-up and magnification photography. They are an excellent choice where one camera must serve for a wide variety of uses. Weight is greater than with the small cameras, but so is versatility. Lens interchangeability is great, and usually convenient. Where economy of film is important, small roll-film adapters are readily available and are convenient to use.

If mobility is not a factor but highest quality large prints and extreme adjustability in use are necessary, the best choice is a view camera. These cameras are also well adapted to the needs of work of high magnification. A view camera consists essentially of a support base, usually a single rail or a folding flat bed, with tracks, surmounted by a film-holding back and a lens-carrying front, each so constructed as to be to some extent three-dimensionally adjustable. Front and back are, of course, connected by the usual bellows (see Figure 2). They are readily available in sizes using 4 × 5, 5 × 7, and 8 × 10 inch film. Both smaller and larger sizes can be had, but this range best covers the needs to be discussed here. The one great advantage of the view camera, other than sheer size, is that one can move all of the elements of the camera front and camera back with relation to one another and the subject matter. This allows correction and adjustment of perspective and the chance to increase greatly the apparent depth of field through manipulation of the lens position and its accompanying principal plane of focus. For architectural photography and for many studio uses this type of camera is essential. Though some notes on them will appear later, there will be no attempt to survey comprehensively the movements and uses of view cameras. Those needing this special information are referred to the excellent references in the Bibliography.

Disadvantages of view cameras are that hand-held use is impractical, and their operation in general is relatively slow. The cost of film, in individual sheets, is relatively high, but it is compensated for (at least in part) because there is usually less need or casual inclination for multiple exposures to "be sure." And even 8 × 10 inch films are cheap enough so that the additional cost is more than recompensed by the increased quality of result. For general laboratory-based work, view cameras offer such great qualitative advantages that wherever space and other circumstances allow, and the need for mobility is not imperative, their use is highly recommended.

Camera Supports

For the best and sharpest results with *any* camera, a tripod or other firm camera support is necessary wherever practicable. But just any tripod will not do. Even small cameras need a tripod which is strong and sturdy enough to resist wind vibration and other stresses. So choose wisely. Big-camera tripods must be fairly sturdy simply to carry the weight, but the very small light tripods often suggested for use with 35-mm cameras are very frequently so unstable and vibration-prone as to be worse than useless. *Camera movement during exposure is probably the single greatest cause of picture unsharpness.* Even with quite high shutter speeds and careful attention to camera-holding technique, there is a distinct and visible difference between hand-held and tripod-held pictures. Because poorly designed tripods are quite likely to be least dependable just when most needed and because sharpness is one of the more important characteristics of research photography, great care in the choice of a tripod is necessary.

3

QUALITY

The matter of quality in the making of a photograph for purposes of illustration is something which has so far been stressed without being thoroughly explained. Top-quality work for scientific purposes, while varying in some elements according to subject matter and circumstances, has certain common features. These are sharpness, separation, and clarity. By "sharpness" is meant the ability to distinguish a maximum amount of fine detail. "Separation" refers to the ability to determine clearly the boundaries of the important subject matter against its background and against and between its own various parts, without apparent blending of tones in any important areas. "Clarity" is the presentation of the relevant subject matter without excess extraneous intrusions and without ambiguity. Part of this presentation is the placing of the subject of main importance within the bounds of the picture area. If this main subject is small relative to the area shown, it should usually be placed in a central position. If not placed centrally, the subsidiary portions of the picture should be arranged where practical to lead the eye to the main subject. Composition, as this arrangement of the picture content is usually called, should, then, be simple and straightforward. Because of what we may call "the human principle of misunderstanding wherever possible," complex or subtle arrangements should be avoided unless the nature of the subject matter requires it. With the aid of a brief caption it should always be possible to see at once what is being pointed out without likelihood of misunderstanding (see various Plates for illustrations of above).

Quality of the end product is obtained through constant attention to detail, but if the necessary requirements are held clearly in mind it is possible to achieve quality without being fanatic about technical expertise, particularly since the individual worker's needs and usages will usually be relatively limited. Achieving quality will greatly enhance both the appearance and the scientific value of any presentation requiring illustration. Coupled with a neat and orderly arrangement of subject matter within the picture area prior to photography, the steps required for good picture results are suitable equipment used with care, careful lighting, correct exposure, suitable processing of the film, and quality printing of the resulting negative.

Negative Quality

A negative of good quality is the first aim of all black-and-white photography, for a print—while subject to some manipulation—can show only what is already in the negative. Tomes can be and have been written on the subject, but only the essentials will be covered here (see Bibliography for further coverage).

A good negative is, quite simply, one which has a sharp, clear image of the subject matter, is of sufficient density to contain all the tones of the subject without being so dense as to reduce highlight contrast and require unusually long printing time, is not excessively grainy, and has its range of tonal gradations kept consistent with the ability of the various types of printing paper to reproduce them. (Films can encompass a vastly greater range of tones than printing papers.)

Negative density is controlled by the degree of exposure, and has been discussed already.

The nature of the photographic process makes grain in some degree an integral part of the negative. It is not, however, a part of the subject matter, and so the presence of an excessively large and visible grain pattern must be avoided wherever there is the possibility that its presence might render the appearance of any part of the picture in some way ambiguous. In the negative, visible grain is due to the random grouping of the silver grains—themselves microscopic in size—which actually form the image in the film emulsion. Excessive grain can be due to any of several causes. Faster films are generally grainier than slow ones. Overexposure and overdevelopment can also result in enlarged grain, while the high-contrast printing required to provide a good appearance with underexposed negatives also increases the contrast and hence the visibility of such grain as is present. Unusually high processing temperatures and overvigorous developers also tend to increase grain size. And lastly, projection printing enlarges the grain structure just as it does the rest of the image.

Negative contrast is controlled in several places and ways. First of all, it is controlled in the selection of the film to be used. Fast films tend to be lower in over-all contrast than slower ones, although the difference is quite unimportant except in special cases. The major area of control over picture contrasts is in the lighting of the subject. Then there are variations of contrast according to the degree of exposure. Any undue over- or underexposure will excessively lower contrasts in any black-and-white film. It will also tend to distort the range of tonal values; overexposure will dull highlight contrasts and underexposure will dull and greatly diminish shadow detail. Negative contrasts can also be changed about in many instances, depending upon the nature of the subject, through the use of color filters. Finally, contrasts in the final result can be varied within quite broad limits in printing.

Generally speaking, the best negative is one which has had the minimum amount of exposure which will provide *complete* tonal coverage of the subject.

Print Quality

For scientific purposes the best print is one that reveals the maximum amount of significant information about the subject while presenting an attractive visual impression. And the attractive appearance must be subordinate to the significant detail. If a picture does not show all that is desired, it doesn't matter how superficially fine it may appear to the uninformed viewer.

In normal photographic practice—covered, again, only in its essentials, with additional information available through Bibliography references—a good print is said to have a just discernible detailing visible in its brightest highlight areas, a wide range of intermediate tones, and good shadow or dark-area detail with darkest tones just approaching total blackness. Such a print makes a good visual impression; that is, it looks "right."

This practice also generally applies in scientific photography; but sometimes it may be necessary to keep more detail in all areas, and here one may have to print to a slightly lower than normal contrast, producing light-gray highlight areas and dark-gray dark areas for a slightly muddy-looking but informationally complete picture. However, this contingency should happen but rarely, and such practice should not be overdone. The particular need must decide what to do.

Changes in print appearance are brought about through varying print exposure time (lighter or darker by shorter or longer times) and by choice of paper grade (by using papers having more or less contrast to compensate for deficiencies in the negative's contrasts).

Printing papers are made in a variety of contrast grades, the range being represented by steps labeled 0 through 5 (and in one case 6). The low numbers are low in contrast, the high numbers high in contrast. Numbers 2 and 3 represent the expected norm. The paper grade used depends upon the degree of contrast in the negative relative to that desired in the print, of course, and the method of judging correctness is that already described, above. Detailed information on darkroom technology will not be presented here, as it would require too much space just to cover what has already been very well covered in the references listed in the Bibliography. These sources are inexpensive as well as good. (See Plate I for examples of variations in printing technique and the Plates in general for examples of suitable print quality.)

Normal practice is to use glossy surfaced papers (either fully glossed or just air-dried to a semigloss) for publication, and matte surfaces for wall display. Printers prefer the glossy, but matte surfaces reduce the problem of unwanted surface reflections when viewed under uncertain lighting, as in display uses.

PART
II

General Techniques

4

BACKGROUNDS

It may at first seem peculiar to discuss backgrounds before troubling to talk about the subject, but in reality it is a most logical thing to do. For scientific illustration, the background serves an immediate and important function: isolating the subject and focusing the attention of the viewer upon it. It should be uncluttered, impossible to confuse with the subject, and well suited to the techniques of printing and publication.

Due to their peripheral and, if well done, inconspicuous nature, backgrounds are too frequently not considered in the planning of a picture. The result is often a poorly differentiated subject, scarcely visible as an important and separate entity. Both the importance of its function and the logical planning of a picture setup demand early full consideration of background problems.

Types of backgrounds are much more limited in kind, nature, and purpose than are subjects. In black-and-white photography there are only four types. These are white, black, gray, and natural—that is, existing as part of the subject material and unalterable by the nature of the situation. Backgrounds for color work will be discussed later in a separate section on Color.

Techniques

PLAIN WHITE BACKGROUNDS

Plain white backgrounds, where practical, are generally to be desired over others because they serve particularly well to isolate the subject and, at the same time, reproduce best in printing. A background which prints photographically as a pure white will, unless given special treatment by the engraver, reproduce as a very light gray, and serves very well as noted above.

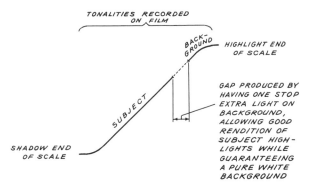

Figure 3. *Tonality scale break with white background*

No matter how a white background is achieved, it will print photographically as pure white only if it receives about 100% (one stop) more light than the subject, unless that subject is unusually dark. Thus, if we see the progression of tones in the final picture as an angled line, this difference will produce in effect a gap in that line, clearly setting off even the highlight areas against the background (Figure 3).

This method of separating the subject from the background has a side effect which can be quite useful. As Figure 3 shows, the highlight areas (and, incidentally, the shadow areas) of a negative are normally slightly less contrasty than are the middle tones. By introducing this "gap" in the tonal range, we place the highlight areas of the actual subject matter down into the more contrasty middle tone areas of the negative, rather than up on the relatively low-contrast "shoulder" of the curve. Thus a greater degree of highlight contrast will be present in the final print. For best use of this effect, a good degree of accuracy of exposure and control of lighting contrasts is necessary, but this is not really difficult if one is careful and makes knowledgeable use of his equipment.

For large subjects photographed outdoors, and where a natural background is for some reason undesirable, the easiest way to achieve a white background is to use the sky, particularly if the day is overcast. The background will then be at least very light, and if conditions are right it will print pure white. The additional light necessary to provide a pure white in the print can be obtained either by turning the subject so that the brightest part of the sky is behind it (on an overcast day or if one is working in a shaded area), or by using a light blue filter to reproduce the blue sky as white (see later section on Filters for detail). Such filtering can also have the effect of "removing" unwanted scattered small clouds.

When subjects are moderately large in size, the background—whether white paper, cloth, or other material—can be placed vertically behind the subject at a little distance. Then the lighting is either so arranged as to provide the necessary extra background light, or a double exposure can be made with little or no light on the subject during the second exposure. To avoid confusing shadows, lighting fixtures should be placed off the optical axis and enough distance kept between subject and background to allow the shadows to pass off to one side. A top view of a typical setup would appear as in Figure 4.

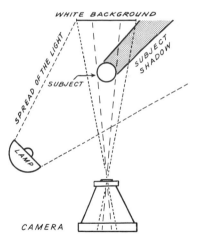

Figure 4. *Basic horizontal camera setup*

The great majority of research-type subjects are quite small, and in most cases are most easily photographed under a vertically mounted camera. The most convenient method of producing a white background here is to suspend a sheet of glass some distance above the background, lay the subject on it, and photograph it (Figure 5). This method works well even at the highest magnifications to be discussed here.

It will be found useful to construct one or more glass-topped tables in sizes

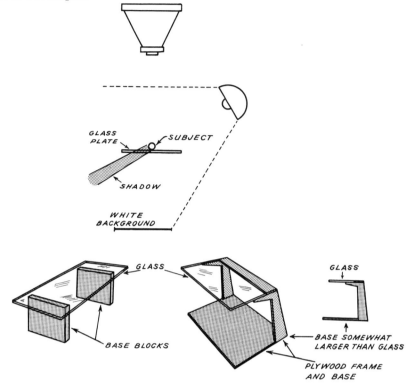

Figure 5. *Basic vertical camera setup, with designs for the glass-topped table used*

suited to your subject matter. These can be anywhere from an inch or two high to perhaps 2 feet high, with glass tops of from 1 × 3 inches to about 20 × 24 inches or more. Two useful forms are illustrated in Figure 5.

Another method of getting a background that prints white is useful when the lighting is axial or near-axial—that is, approaching the subject from the direction of the camera lens—and the subject is not larger than a few inches in size. In this case, use a sheet of household aluminum foil for the background, and lay the subject directly upon it. Such foil is mirror-bright on one side and slightly matte on the other. If it is shiny side up, it will reflect into the camera an image of the light source. But if it is matte side up, the result is a fine soft glow surrounding the subject (see Plate XI-A as an illustration and Figure 6 for the setup of the equipment). There will probably be a slight penumbra of shadow visible around the subject but, unless the subject is unusually light or bright, even this will be white in the print. In any case it will not be so dark as to disturb the eye or confuse the edge of the subject. This setup is particularly useful with coins and medallions (see later section on Special Subject Matter).

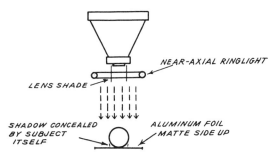

Figure 6. *Using aluminum foil to obtain a white background with near-axial lighting*

Wherever a white background is used, it is necessary to limit the size of the background so that it covers an area not much larger than the subject. If it is too large, there will be two difficulties. First, the background will reflect so much extra light to the lens that there will be internal flare inside the camera, having the effect of drastically lowering the over-all contrasts of the picture. (This will also be the case if the background delivers too much light to the camera—that is, much over 100% more than the subject.) Second, in any but two-dimensional subjects a too large background causes disturbing edge reflections on the subject (see Plate VIII-A).

It is possible to obtain white backgrounds by using internally lighted boxes topped with a sheet of opal glass, and such items are commercially available; however, these are relatively inflexible in use and are usually quite expensive.

BLACK BACKGROUNDS

Black backgrounds have somewhat more limited usefulness because they are difficult to reproduce well in any but printing of high quality. Poorer quality printing—unfortunately present in many of the less well financed journals—results in grayness and in breaks that produce quantities of white spots instead of a uniform black area. For sheer drama of presentation, however, black backgrounds are unbeatable in either color or black-and-white. They are also very desirable for good appearance wherever the subject is either white or very light in color.

The single best material for black backgrounds is a good grade of deep-nap velvet or velveteen—quite expensive but worth it. The necessity here is for a material which reflects virtually no light at all, to assure separation from the subject matter. No other material approaches deep-nap velvet; even shallow-nap velvets are poor, and napless cloth or black paper is very poor.

A secondary method of achieving deep black is a glass topped box with black lining, but this often results in reflections of camera and/or subject on the glass surface. Some variation of this may be necessary if the subject is wet or needs to be immersed in water. If the background is really black, if edge separations are clear, and if the negative is large enough (4 × 5 or over), the offending reflection images can be physically scraped off the negative without damage to the final print quality.

If velvet is used, the subject is simply placed directly upon it. Shadows cast by the subject will be absorbed directly into the general blackness of the background. No spatial separation will be needed.

Other than problems of journal printing quality, the only big trouble with black backgrounds is to light the subject so as to assure that shadowed areas will not merge into the general black of the background. This will be dealt with later, under Lighting, but a good rule to follow is to see that the subject's shadows are only just discernible to the eye. If lighted properly, the shadowed areas will then appear natural in the print and still differentiate at edges.

PLAIN GRAY BACKGROUNDS

Plain gray backgrounds are generally to be avoided. In journal reproduction a white background—unless specially treated—prints as a light gray. Gray backgrounds, then, will reproduce as darker grays, and the result is usually unpleasantly muddy in appearance, with the subject itself difficult to differentiate. The commonest reason for using a plain gray background is to best show a subject having both white and black areas in it, such as a white root with some branches blackened by disease. Unfortunately, there will generally be transitional areas connecting the two where the subject color merges with the gray of the background. This can sometimes erroneously appear as a break in the subject; hence gray should be avoided here, too. In most such cases the actual best rendering is against a white background, with the white subject areas printed as a light gray.

NATURAL BACKGROUNDS

Natural backgrounds, as earlier noted, are used when the background exists as part of the subject material or is for some reason an unalterable condition of the situation. There may also be cases where a natural background is simply the most desirable one, for scientific accuracy, the preference of the worker, or other reasons. Differentiation between the naturally occurring background and the main subject can then be achieved by several means, and you should pay careful attention to its achievement.

For relatively small subjects, an excellent—and in many cases virtually unavoidable—way you can do it is to take advantage of the inherently shallow depth of field found where image magnification is relatively great. You can readily have the main subject sharply in focus, while all or nearly all other parts of the picture are out of focus. The observer's eye is naturally drawn to the in-focus portion, and so to the intended main subject (see Plate II-D).

A second method of differentiation between subject and background is through color. If one is dark and the other light there is no problem. If both are relatively similar in brightness but are different in color—that is, if they are of colors which will be reproduced by panchromatic films as similar shades of gray—you can use color filters to cause an apparent light-and-dark difference in the final picture (see later section on Filters; see also Plate II-C).

Where the color of the subject and background is similar and there is too little spatial separation to allow differentiation by focus, you can use light to make the difference. You can either use a grazing direct light (to show the shape and texture of the subject) or cause a shadow to fall behind or under the subject and thereby show it as light against a darker background (see Plate II-A and B).

Nearly any problem of differentiation can be solved by one of these methods, or by using them in combination. In difficult situations only informed experimentation will find the solution.

5

LIGHTING

As the name "photography" implies, the most important and complex single feature of the craft as practiced here is the application of light to the subject. Unless the subject is suitably lit, the purpose of the photograph—exposure of the salient and significant features of that subject to the final observer—will not be accomplished. Lighting must be applied according to a knowledge of what it will do in terms of film and photo-paper response, in terms of the final picture.

First to be decided is the nature of the background, as already stated. Then the subject must be correctly oriented to the light. It is important that the light in the picture should appear to come roughly from the top. Whether from directly above, or from top left or top right, is—except in cases where convention decrees—relatively unimportant, but it must be generally from the top. If lit from what will be picture bottom, the appearance of relief will be optically deceptive. Hills will appear to be valleys, and vice versa. Relief will be apparently reversed. This can be confirmed by looking at pictures containing relief lighting effects while turning them at various angles.

Steps must often be taken to protect the subject matter, especially small plant and animal materials, from the heat of the lights. This is accomplished by introducing between lamp and subject a water cell, a transparent-sided water-filled container which absorbs the heat rays while passing the visible light rays. This is especially necessary if a high light intensity is required (as with high magnification work), and if a light-concentrating lens has been used.

A typical setup using such a lens and water cell is shown in Figure 7. A simple hand magnifier with its handle clamped to a common lab stand will serve admirably to increase light levels, but will literally shrivel up an insect or leaf if a water cell 3–4 inches thick is not interposed.

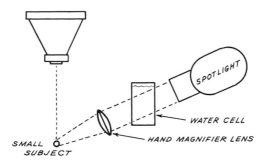

Figure 7. *Lighting of small objects, cooled with water cell*

For a thorough understanding of lighting technique it is necessary to keep several principles clearly in mind. One is known as the law of reflection: the angle at which a beam of light is reflected from a surface (the angle of reflection) is equal to the angle at which it hits that surface (the angle of incidence); see Figure 8. Thorough understanding of this principle will solve many of your lighting problems.

Figure 8. *The law of reflection*

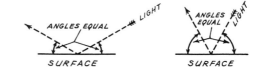

A second principle to remember is this: in black-and-white photography apparent lighting contrasts are vastly increased by putting them on film and then on paper. What appears to the eye to be a just discernible shadowing becomes in the final print a very respectable shadow indeed. This is because the range of illumination that the eye can record is vastly greater than that of the film; and the film's range is greater than that of the printing paper. Because of this, a degree of shadowing *distinctly* visible to the eye will risk losing detail in what will become deep shade in the final print. And what is deep shade to the eye will be opaque black shadow in the print. The development of a subtle eye for the detection of light and shade will be a great aid in research photography. It should result inevitably if practiced enough. (A simple way of seeing light and shade much as the print will record it is to squint your eyes and look through your lashes. You will find that *detail* disappears; the subject is seen as a mass or group of masses, and the *areas* of light and shadow are more readily seen.)

A third point to keep in mind is that light on a three-dimensional subject should appear to come from one direction only—to avoid ambiguity in relief and a confusing multiplicity of shadows. Thus, any supplementary lighting should generally be slightly weaker than the main light, and probably also more diffuse. This leads, of course, to a general preference for simplicity in lighting setups, which has the obvious advantages of being quick and easy and of requiring less investment in both equipment and space required for its use. Exceptions will later be pointed out.

The exact type of lighting used on a particular job depends upon the nature of the subject and upon what is to be shown of it. Lighting for scientific subject matter is for the purpose of revealing maximum significant detail, of giving maximum significant information. The individual worker must determine what he considers significant in each case before proceeding.

Generally speaking, there are two aspects of the subject, one of which it will be desirable to emphasize—either shape or color. In black-and-white photography, one big pitfall is the danger of confusing the differences between the two by poor lighting. If one is not careful, a light color may appear as a highlight or a dark color as a shadow, or vice versa. Lighting must surely indicate which is which.

Shape is shown either by casting shadows or by using a lighting which will present light to the lens of the camera differentially according to the angle at which the various portions of the subject surface are inclined to that lens. Colors are shown best in black-and-white by so reducing the light-shade contrasts that relief is scarcely noticeable in the final print; thus the various shades of gray in the picture are all accounted for by color differences in the subject. In color photography the problem is, of course, nearly negligible. Colors are clearly colors.

For most purposes here it is preferable to use the steady beams of light provided by natural light or by such artificial sources as floods and spotlights. It is then possible to observe exactly the fall of the light under all circumstances. But the use of flash, either ordinary flash bulbs or electronic flash, can be very useful for stopping action or other special purposes. Where flash is used, you must be especially careful in determining the angle of lighting, since it cannot usually be directly observed prior to the exposure.

Calculation of flash exposures is made by resorting to a standard formula:

$$\text{f-value} = \frac{\text{guide number}}{\text{lamp-subject distance (feet)}}$$

or, in abbreviated form,

$$\text{f-v} = \frac{gn}{d_{lp-sub}}$$

The guide number is a constant provided in the flash source data sheet, and takes into account the film speed and the exposure time to be used. When divided by the lamp-to-subject distance (*not* the camera-to-subject distance), the product yielded is the f-value or diaphragm opening, to be used to gain a correct exposure. As the guide numbers are approximate, specific testing may be necessary for critical use. But for most normal use such special testing is not required.

Techniques

There are for our purposes only a few really different lighting setups. We will take these up in the order of their usual importance.

REFLECTOR AND DIFFUSER LIGHTING

This type of lighting consists of one lamp inclined downward onto the subject, with a tissue paper diffuser on the lamp side of the subject and a white card reflector on the other side (see Figure 9).

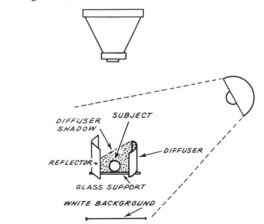

Figure 9. *Reflector-diffuser lighting*

With this setup one can vary the lighting contrasts of the subject almost indefinitely by moving either the reflector or the diffuser back and forth to suit. The range is from entirely equal light from both sides to a bright highlight opposed to a deep shadow. The effect can readily be observed during these adjustments by placing the eye at the camera position. Where the subject matter is irregularly shaped, it may prove desirable to use small subsidiary reflectors to add light to certain areas not well enough illuminated otherwise. This may be particularly likely when using black backgrounds, in order to keep subject shadows light enough to separate from the background in printing.

This setup is the most generally useful one. The diffuser keeps the light relatively soft and free of harshness, and the reflector fills in the shadow side to any degree desired. Reference to the text figure will show that, while the subject is completely shaded by the diffuser, the reflector is at least partly directly lit. This allows fuller flexibility and control than is possible if it is completely shaded.

Note, too, that the text figure shows a white background which is completely unshaded by the diffuser. Direct background light in this setup provides the extra 100% of light to allow it to print pure white in the final picture, in all but the lightest colored of subjects. (Those subjects which are extremely light may need a certain amount of extra background lighting to assure complete separation in printing.) The basic setup is, of course, also perfectly usable with any other type of background.

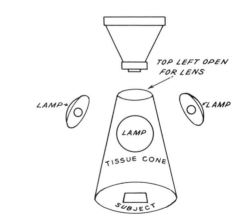

Figure 10.   *Light tenting*

This general arrangement will serve for a very wide range of subject matter types and should be tried first when in doubt. It can be used at high magnification, as well as for subjects as large as a watermelon. It is a particularly good method to use where low lighting contrasts are needed in order to emphasize color over shape, although shape can also be shown well simply by moving the reflector back to raise lighting contrast (see Figure 10).

Where the only important feature of the subject is color, but where the shape is very irregular or the surface heavily textured, a variation of this method—the "light tent"—is useful. Light tenting is also useful with small bright metal objects where harsh surface reflections must be subdued. In this arrangement a truncated cone of white tissue paper extends from the lens to, or below, the subject, and is commonly lit from two or three sides to equalize intensities. A complete lack of shadows and an absolutely even distribution of light results in subject differentiation by color alone; shape—except, of course, for outline—is visually nullified. With small subject matter this effect can be gained by using ordinary reflector-diffuser lighting, but with both reflector and diffuser relatively large and close to the subject and wrapped well around it. See Plate III, A and B, for specific illustrations; see Plates IX, C and D, and XIV, D, for other examples of similar lighting.

DIRECT LIGHTING

The second most versatile setup is plain old direct lighting. This resembles, in practice, the reflector-diffuser method just discussed, except that there is no diffuser (see Figure 11).

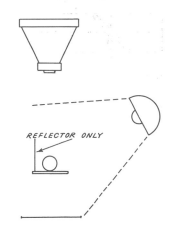

Figure 11. *Direct lighting*

A reflector will generally be necessary on the shadowed side, if shadow detail is to be retained at all. In this case it is unlikely that complete equality of lighting is obtainable unless the reflector is a mirror (a useful technique itself upon occasion, see later sections), but good control of contrasts can still be obtained. As the usual reflector material is a matte white card, the usual fill-in light returned to the subject is soft and diffuse; thus the directionality of light is clearly maintained even when near-equality of intensity is used (see Plate III-C). Again, small subsidiary reflectors may be needed for best results with irregular subjects. This setup is excellent for showing surface textures, as well as for showing low and medium height relief. The lower the relief to be shown, the lower the angle of the lamp.

With this setup a pure white background requires either a separate or brighter (or closer) lamp on the background. Alternatively, the subject can be shaded during part of the exposure by a circle of standing black cards. Black backgrounds require no special treatment.

AXIAL AND NEAR-AXIAL LIGHTING

A specialized application of direct lighting is involved in axial and near-axial lighting. To say that light is "axial" means that it comes or appears to come from the direction of the camera itself—that is, along the optical axis.

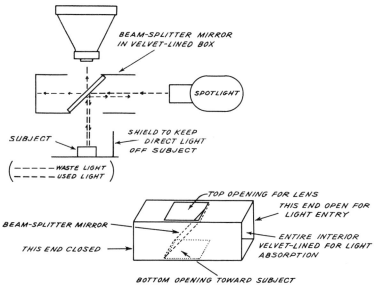

Figure 12. *Axial lighting by means of a beam-splitter*

To obtain this effect, a half-silvered mirror or a plain optical flat is used as a beam-splitter, and is mounted at a 45° angle in the center of a box which is open at one end. This box serves to cut out light or reflections from other than the intended source, as well as to absorb the light that passes through the beam-splitter (Figure 12). One hole is in the top of the box over the mirror, and another is in the bottom under it. The box must be entirely lined with black velvet to cut out all stray reflections. The use of a beam-splitter results in at least a 75% light loss, for at each of the two impingements of the light beam upon the mirror less than 50% passes through and the rest is reflected off or absorbed in passing through (see light path in Figure 12).

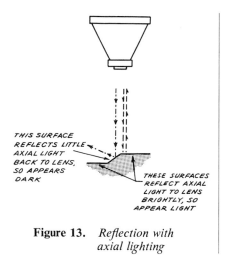

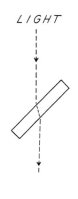

Figure 13. *Reflection with axial lighting*

Figure 14. *Offset of a beam of light by refraction*

Axial lighting is used for two purposes: (1) where deep cavities must be lit from outside (Plate III, D and E), and (2) in use of the law of reflection, to indicate very low relief (Plate XI, B). Statement (2) simply means that surfaces inclined to the lens will reflect less light to that lens than will a surface at right angles to the axis of the lens (and at right angles to the light, in axial lighting). The effect will be harsh, and will thus exaggerate and thereby tend to show better very low reliefs (Figure 13).

Beam-splitters must be optically flat or severe distortion of the image will result. Some linear distortion will probably be present in all but the very best of these mirrors, because the beam of light is offset by refraction (Figure 14), and any imperfections will thereby be exaggerated. Thinner glass will give less such distortion by giving less offset. In work at high magnification by this method use the thinnest available microscope slide cover glass as a mirror.

This method of lighting, as earlier noted, can be used to light very deep cavities, as well as objects within them, where no other method can accomplish it. It is also particularly good where one must show relief so low as to be virtually undetectable. For other usages the lighting provided may well be too harsh.

Near-axial lighting is, of course, lighting from a source close to but not at the optical axis. It can be achieved by using a light actually placed close to the camera lens (Figure 15, A), by using a mirror placed close to the camera lens to reflect a beam of light correctly (Figure 15, B), or by using a ringlight (either a fluorescent ring or an electronic flash ringlight) surrounding the lens (Figure 15, C). The lens in this last case must be shielded from the stray light.

Near-axial lighting is useful for penetration of moderately deep cavities or, with the ringlights, for indicating very low relief with less harshness than with beam-splitter axial lighting (see p. 33), or for giving an even, soft, shadowless, nondirectional light. In this last instance, it should be emphasized, only the ringlight is suitable—not the first two near-axial methods. Where practical,

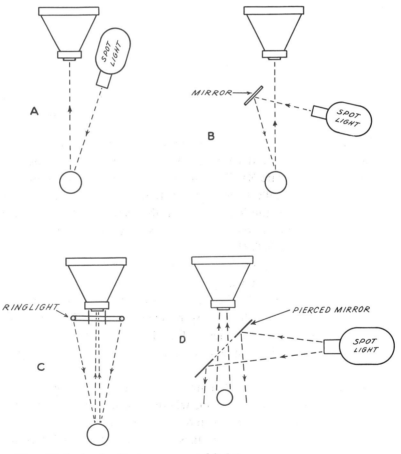

Figure 15. *Methods of achieving near-axial lighting*

these methods of lighting are to be preferred over true axial lighting, since one can avoid optical aberrations and the problem of light loss. Fluorescent ringlights are not recommended for color work (see later section on Color for details).

For small subjects the effect of a ringlight can be well simulated by using a special mirror—pierced by a hole and mounted at a 45° angle just below the lens—illuminated by a spotlight off to one side (Figure 15, D). A convenient way of making such a setup is to use as a mirror a small rectangle of household aluminum foil with a hole cut in it. The foil rectangle is mounted at a 45° angle between lens and subject, the lens views through the hole, and the light is reflected down, ring-fashion, upon the subject. The dull side of the foil should face the subject in order to distribute the light more evenly. The shiny side tends to produce "hot spots" of light.

This lighting method is particularly useful where a small subject sits directly on a natural background and where no hint of shadow can be allowed, due to danger of obscuring edges or other important detail.

For any of the methods of near-axial lighting, the backgrounds can be either black or white, as desired. With either the ringlight or the pierced mirror, a sheet of aluminum foil can be used to produce a white background (see Figure 6 and accompanying text, p. 23). With the near-axial lighting schemes of Figure 15, A and B, the directed light beam falls so as to make white backgrounding difficult, but it can be accomplished by placing the subject on a glass plate above a white card, and illuminating that card separately with another lamp. Where a large fluorescent ringlight is used to provide soft nondirectional light upon a moderately large object, the best method is probably just to lay the subject directly on a white card. The background will be very nearly white in the final print, with just a tinge of off-white if the subject is light-colored. Shadowing here will most likely not be present at all, and in the worst of cases it will be no more than a very pale penumbra. (This shadowing can be minimized by constructing and using a multiple lamp. Fluorescent rings come in three sizes, which can be mounted concentrically for this purpose.) Black backgrounds offer no difficulties; the subject is simply laid directly upon a piece of velvet, as usual.

TRANSMITTED LIGHT

Transmitted light as used in scientific photography is either an optically aligned beam or diffuse light. The commonest use of transmitted light is in photomicrography of mounted slides, where the aligned beam is normal. This usage will not be treated here, since it is well covered elsewhere (see Bibliography), but diffuse transmitted light will be of interest.

For any translucent or transparent subject, such as geological thin sections, thin leaves, or tissue sections (Plate IV), or for making copies of color transparencies (Plate XVI, A), a convenient way of producing diffuse transmitted light is to light a matte white card which has been placed a little distance behind the subject, which itself receives no direct light at all. With a vertical camera the setup is the same as for reflector-diffuser lighting with a white background, except that the subject is surrounded with a standing ring of black cards to keep all top light off it.

DARK-FIELD LIGHTING

A special application of transmitted light is found in dark-field lighting. In this particular usage the principle is to light the subject from below or behind by light beams which strike the lens only if they are refracted or scattered by the subject. In microscopic use this effect is contrived by introducing a center stop into the back of the condenser and thereby producing a hollow cone of light. We can, with larger subjects, produce a similar effect by placing a ringlight below or behind the subject. If a shield keeps the direct light of the ring from the lens, and if the distance between ring and subject is correctly arranged for maximum effect (by placing one eye at the camera lens position and adjusting the light-to-subject distance and positioning until satisfied), then only that light which is refracted or scattered toward the lens by the subject is effective. The situation is then functionally analogous to the usual microscopic arrangement (see Figure 16).

Figure 16. *Dark-field lighting with ringlight*

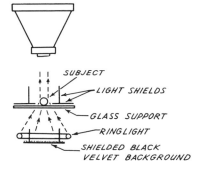

SUBJECT
LIGHT SHIELDS
GLASS SUPPORT
RINGLIGHT
SHIELDED BLACK
VELVET BACKGROUND

By using this method along with some carefully balanced top lighting (either direct or reflector-diffuser illumination), it is possible to display concurrently normally visible surface detail and difficult-to-show edge effects, such as hairs. Care must be taken to correctly balance the two sources so that neither is of such intensity as to dominate and thereby conceal the effects of the other. (With color films, beware of mixing light from a fluorescent ringlight with light from normal tungsten sources, as the color effects may be unpredictable; see later section on Color, p. 67.)

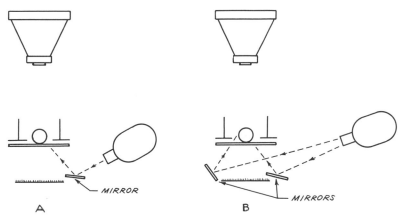

Figure 17. *Directional dark-field lighting with mirrors*

Another variation of dark-field lighting allows directional effects. Instead of using a ringlight behind or below the subject, a mirror is placed below and to one side of the subject. A beam of light is directed onto the mirror and is then reflected up to the subject (Figure 17, A). By turning the subject with respect to the light it is possible to control directionality completely, and thereby show effects which could not be otherwise seen. The technique is particularly useful with some types of geological thin sections. With care this setup can also provide for color work the effect of a dark field or a combination of dark field and top light.

More complex effects can be obtained by using two mirrors, arranged as shown in Figure 17, B. This provides directional dark-field lighting from opposite ends of the subject, both reinforcing the effect and evening it out, while still avoiding any possibility of such light from the sides. If desired, an all-around effect similar to a ringlight, but without the undesirable color effects of a fluorescent ringlight, can be had by using two such double-mirror setups, each with its own lamp, set up at 90° to one another.

For examples of dark-field photography, see Plates V and IX, A.

6

MAGNIFICATIONS

Photographic work at magnifications is a subject that may at first give an impression of great difficulty and mystery. Actually it is neither more nor less difficult or mysterious than any other branch of the craft. No matter what the field, things are primarily difficult and mysterious to those who do not understand. Doing quality work at magnifications does indeed require care and some special equipment and knowledge. Particularities of equipment will be left up to the individual worker after a few general remarks.

Although quite adequate work can often be done using normal camera lenses, a great increase in flatness of field and some increase in resolution can be had by using lenses specially designed for the job. If normal camera lenses must be used, then one should determine the optical design of the one used. A lens that is optically symmetrical can be used just as it is, but one that is optically asymmetrical will usually perform better at magnifications if it is reversed so that the element normally turned toward the film faces toward the subject.

There will be no discussion of supplementary "close-up" lenses, as these work only at the lowest magnifications and always at a sacrifice in optical quality.

A recent development in 35-mm camera circles has been the introduction of an number of "macro" and "micro" type lenses built for use with specific cameras. (Many such lenses are not true micro lenses even when so titled, but are simply very good quality general-purpose lenses in extended-range focusing mounts.) These lenses have been quite fully appraised and discussed in the photographic press, the general conclusion being that all of the lenses of this type now out seem excellent for use in a range between ×1 and about ×10. (I have seen no discussions of uses for these lenses at higher magnification, so I can not discuss them.) These lenses are usually equipped with an unusually long focusing range, built into the lens mount to allow an approach to ×1 without extra extensions such as tubes or bellows. Automatic or semi-automatic diaphragm action and an aid of some sort in calculating exposures in this low range of magnification are normally built into the lens housing. These devices are handy indeed in this range of work, but beyond ×1 they seem to offer little advantage over other types of macro or micro lenses which are adaptable to any camera. If their use fits your equipment and needs, by all means use them. They are excellent where the need is for an approach within two feet to several inches of the subject, as in following live insects.

For the low to intermediate range of magnifications—from ×1 to around ×10—there is another type of lens which is quite widely used. This is the process lens of 4- to 6-inch focal length. These lenses—the best-known first-class examples being the Goerz Artars—are designed to produce a high degree of color correction, field flatness, and resolution, combined with great freedom from linear and other distortions. They are, however, quite expensive. They normally come in barrel mounts but can be had mounted in shutters. Custom mounting in any available shutter can be done, or shutters can be dispensed with completely if action need not be stopped, exposures then being made with the lens cap or a piece of black card used to control timing. Process lenses are primarily designed for graphic arts reproduction work, but their design makes them very useful here. One noticeable feature of these lenses is their relative slowness, their widest aperture being usually f/9 to f/11. This is seldom a disadvantage, since most work to be discussed here requires stopping down beyond that level anyway in order to obtain depth of field. These process lenses require a long bellows for magnification work.

For work in all ranges from ×1 to about ×80 there were available for many years a series of lenses produced by Zeiss and by Bausch & Lomb called Micro-Tessars. If still available, they will be found quite good; they are of shorter focal lengths than the process lenses, thereby requiring less bellows length for a given magnification. They were barrel mounted and required adaptation to one's equipment, usually a simple matter.

The cream of lenses currently available for use in the range of ×1 to ×80 are the recently introduced Zeiss Luminars, available in five focal lengths: 16, 25, 40, 63, and 100 mm. These lenses produce images which are very sharp, flat in field, and free of distortion, being about equal to process lenses and designed for use at higher magnifications. They are at their sharpest when the diaphragm is wide open. (No lens is equally sharp at all openings; usually a lens is sharpest when stopped about three units smaller than the widest stop.) Excellent sharpness prevails until the very smallest stops are reached, but there is a definite deterioration of the image in the last couple of stops, thereby limiting enlargement possibilities in any negative made when fully stopped down. (It is not intended to downgrade these fine lenses by mentioning the above facts, but rather to provide detailed knowledge of a group of lenses which are the most highly recomended for this type of work. No lenses known to me are superior to these.) In addition to being of high optical quality, these lenses are quite reasonable in price and are much faster than process lenses. While the diaphragm is graduated in a nonstandard fashion—1, 2, 4, 8,. . . instead of f/4, 5.6, 8, 11,. . .— the widest opening is in the range of f/3.5 to f/4.5, depending upon the focal length in use. The difference between stops is the standard 100%. Luminars are barrel mounted, having a standard microscope objective thread on the base—except for the 100-mm size, which is larger. They can thus be used on a photographic microscopic, with suitable condensers, for translucent subjects. No ocular is required. Adaptation to camera use is simple. A set of Luminars of at least the four shorter focal lengths is highly recommended for anyone intending to do a large amount of work at medium to high magnifications.

Those workers preferring to use 35-mm single-lens reflex cameras for this sort of work are encouraged to do so, particularly if the subjects are alive and moving. Where the subject moves little or not at all, however, one would be well advised to use a larger camera and thereby avoid problems in printing and elsewhere. At high magnifications one often teeters on the edge of resolution capabilities, especially when stopped down for reasons of depth of field. Enlarging from negatives made under these conditions may well result in mainly empty magnifications. Viewing, composing, lighting, and exposure calculation may all be found easier with a larger ground glass. As always, equipment choice must be left to the individual worker, who can give due consideration to his own needs and to the demands of his particular requirements.

For work at magnifications, by far the most convenient setup is the vertically mounted camera. This will allow maximum convenience in handling the subject and the lighting fixtures.

Techniques

OBTAINING KNOWN MAGNIFICATIONS

In working at magnifications the first problem is, of course, to determine just what degree of enlargement is necessary. While it may seem obvious to say so, this is best determined by directly measuring the subject area desired and dividing this figure into the size of picture desired. Many workers are used to computing magnifications by multiplying the dissecting scope ocular and objective values. This is fine for visual work, but often leads to inaccuracy in estimating the magnification required for photography.

In photography the magnification of the image is directly related to the focal length of the lens used. It is determined mathematically by dividing the distance between lens and film by the focal length, and subtracting one focal length. At $\times 1$ (actual size) the lens-film distance is two focal lengths. At $\times 2$ it is three focal lengths, at $\times 10$ it is eleven, and at $\times 80$ it is 81 focal lengths. Thus, a lens-film distance of 24 inches, with a lens of 4-inch focal length, yields a magnification of $\times 5$. The formula for calculating magnifications is:

$$\text{magnification} = \frac{\text{lens-film distance minus focal length}}{\text{focal length}}$$

or

$$\text{mag} = \frac{d_{lf} - fl}{fl}$$

For rough work the above formula will suffice. The position of the film, of course, is known, and one assumes that the diaphragm ring is at the center of the lens and that the lens center is the place to measure from. Unfortunately, this is not always the case. Many lenses are optically asymmetrical, and many diaphragms are not located exactly centrally. Where precalculation of exact magnification is not needed, but final dimensions must be known, the above calculations can be used and the picture made, and then a good scale or scale micrometer is either photographed or measured on the ground glass under identical conditions and the exact magnification thereby determined directly.

Exact precalculation of magnification is necessary wherever one wishes to render a given subject at a given final image size. This is best done by putting a scale in the subject position and then adjusting the lens-film distance until measurement with another scale of the ground glass image yields a correct degree of magnification. With small cameras—including reflexes—where there is no ground glass or it is not accessible for direct measurement, the best arrangement is to open the camera back and place a small piece of fine ground glass in the film position *ground side toward the lens*. And if the negative is enlarged subsequently, the magnification must be recalculated by multiplying the camera-set magnification by the degree of enlargement.

If one does much of this sort of work, a great time saver is to calibrate the camera. Two arbitrary points on the camera are chosen, at the front and at the back. Then the camera is set up serially throughout the entire range of magnifications to be used, and measurements between the two points are made and recorded at each magnification. A chart can then be made up, indicating the exact measurement between the points for any magnification desired at any later time. This must be done for each separate lens to be used, of course. It may be found convenient to actually fasten a steel tape to one end of the camera and simply draw it out each time to a single chosen point at the other end of the camera.

PRINCIPAL PLANE OF FOCUS

When a lens is focused on a subject, only a single plane slicing through that subject is truly sharp. (This effect is especially noticeable when working at magnifications.) This plane is called "the principal plane of focus."

A point worth noting here is that, with three-dimensional objects, the magnification will be exact only at the principal plane of focus. If the focus is at the top of the subject, the edge-to-edge distance in the picture will be different than will be the case if the focus is at the center or bottom. Where over-all dimensions are important—that is, if measurements of over-all size are to be made directly from the final print—the principal plane of focus must be at the widest part of the subject (see Figure 18).

Figure 18. *The principal plane of focus*

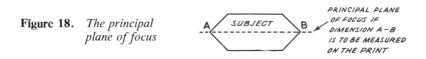

PRINCIPAL PLANE OF FOCUS IF DIMENSION A-B IS TO BE MEASURED ON THE PRINT

PRESERVING MAGNIFICATION WHILE ADJUSTING

Once an exact magnification has been precalculated and set up beforehand, there comes the matter of preserving this exactitude while focusing up and down. If the lens or camera back is moved to correct the focus, the magnification will change, so focusing must be done either by moving the camera as a whole or by moving the subject. Any camera arrangement to be used much should take this into account.

Moving the subject can be done by placing it on a lab jack, a square-platform scissors-type jack designed for this type of manipulation. But extensive movements may well require readjustment of lighting arrangements after every move.

Maximum convenience and speed of operation—important factors if much work is to be done—can be obtained through mounting the camera on a screw-driven or rack-and-pinion driven base which will easily and accurately move the whole camera up and down, while preserving rigidity of mounting both between and during movements. If construction of such an arrangement is undesirable or impractical, it may be found convenient to use as a camera one of several available photographic enlargers which have camera backs available as accessories that permit them to be used also as copy cameras. As a part of the enlarger construction they contain a means for focusing the camera portion as a whole, as well as a provision for varying the lens-film distance. Choose one with a bellows as long as possible, to allow maximum magnification without additional accessories. One or two such enlarger-cameras on the market even have both fine and coarse adjustments, and at least one has the coarse adjustment electrically driven.

DEPTH OF FIELD

Having considered the matters of obtaining and preserving a magnification, we come to the closely related and ever-present problem of depth of field. As earlier noted, when a lens is focused on a subject, only a single plane slicing through that subject is truly sharp. One of the functions of the diaphragm is to provide a degree of adjustment in the apparent thickness of this plane. If the diaphragm is stopped down to a smaller opening (all focusing normally being done with it wide open for maximum visibility and accuracy of focus), parts of the subject on either side of the principal plane of focus will become sharp also, and this effect increases as the diaphragm is closed down further. (When initially trying out a new lens, one should make sure that the focus does not change when the diaphragm is stopped down.) This is the method for increasing depth of field, and intelligent handling of it allows one to control with great accuracy just what will or will not be shown sharply in the final picture. For greatest depth of field you should usually focus about one-third of the way into the area you wish to have sharp, as depth of field extends further behind the principal plane of focus than it does before it.

There are limits, of course, to what can be done. One can only stop down so far, and a thick subject at high magnification may not be entirely in focus even at the end of the scale. A second built-in limitation is that all lenses are sharpest at one given aperture. But just where they are sharpest varies among lenses. Luminars, as noted above, are sharpest when wide open, but most camera lenses are at their best about three stops down from their widest opening. After the maximum-resolution opening is reached, further closing down results in image degradation—slight at first, but becoming greater as the size of the aperture diminishes. In some cases a point may be reached where further increase in depth of field may be valueless because of the over-all image degradation. At extremely small apertures, then, the appearance of this image degradation must be carefully watched for. With extremely fast camera lenses the same effect may occur badly at openings *wider* than the optimum setting. (For further information on optical matters, see Bibliography.)

One of the commonest misconceptions with regard to depth of field is that it is greater with short focal length lenses than it is with long ones. This is not so. There are only two variables in depth of field. One can *increase* depth of field by stopping down the diaphragm or by decreasing the image magnification. One can *decrease* depth of field by opening the diaphragm or by increasing the image magnification. Thus, *depth of field is a function of the relationship between the diaphragm opening and the image magnification.* The misconception arises because, *from a given subject-camera distance,* a short focal length lens gives a smaller degree of image magnification and consequently more depth at a given aperture. The depth comes from the image size, and not from the shorter lens. If the images are of like magnification and the f-stop identical, then the depth of field is identical regardless of focal length.

WORKING DISTANCE

Another factor in magnification work is "working distance." Working distance is the distance between lens and subject when the camera is focused. It is a value that one must know beforehand at least approximately if a setup is not to require an inordinate amount of time and frustration. At high magnifications one must be fairly near to a correct focus even to be able to see and locate the subject. The working distance is, like the lens-film distance, related to the focal length of the lens being used. At $\times 1$ it is the same as the lens-film distance—that is, twice the focal length of the lens. As the magnification increases the working distance decreases rapidly until it approaches, at around $\times 3$–4, the focal length of the lens. After that it approaches that value more and more slowly, getting ever closer to but never quite reaching the measure of the focal length of the lens being used (see Figure 19). For practical purposes, by $\times 3$ one simply sets the camera so that the lens is about its own focal length from the subject. Then, watching the ground glass, the camera is focused until the image is sharp.

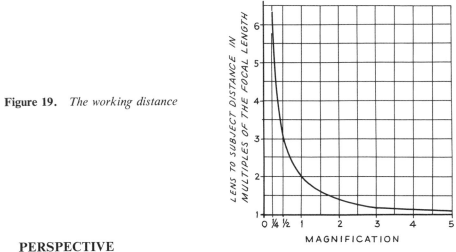

Figure 19. *The working distance*

PERSPECTIVE

In this business of working at magnifications there should be mention of choosing a lens of the correct focal length, if such a choice is available. The matter is quite simply put, and for simple reasons. Figuring from how much magnification is needed and how much lens-film distance is possible with one's equipment (that is, how long a bellows or other extension is possible), one uses the lens of longest possible focal length.

A long lens gives a longer working distance, with less apparent image distortion of three-dimensional objects, or better perspective. As Figure 20 indicates,

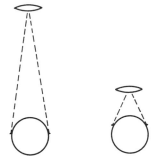

Figure 20. *Effects of perspective with lenses of long focus and short focus*

there is a truer picture of the actual dimensions and shape of the subject with the lens of longer focus. The shorter the lens the more likely it will be to represent the nearest portion of the subject as unreasonably large, compared to the further portions, since with such a short lens the lens-subject (or working) distance is likely to be very short also. And when the working distance is so short, the lens sees less far around the contours.

The second reason for using the longest possible lens is to use the resulting longer working distance to provide ample room for the proper placing of lights, diffusers, and other fixtures of the setup.

SPECIAL DIFFICULTIES

Lighting. In the course of making small things large through photography, one runs into certain special difficulties. One of these is the matter, once again, of lighting. Actually, the methods of lighting described earlier are as applicable here as they are elsewhere. But since the subject is small, so must the fixtures be small. If reflectors and diffusers are overly large they may, especially if badly angled, produce too much light scatter, with consequent flare inside the camera. This may tend to lower contrasts and give generally poor-looking results. This is a matter for close observation during the setup, rather than one of hard-and-fast rules, but the possibility should not be overlooked. Some setups, such as light tenting, demand fixtures which are large compared to the subject. Where they are used, watch the set-up carefully and correct where necessary.

More than in other types of photography, the intensity of light required here is of great importance. According to physical law, "light falls off as the square of the distance." For example, a light source will throw only one-fourth as much light on the subject if the lamp-subject distance is doubled. This rule also holds inside the camera. When a camera is focused at infinity, the lens-film distance equals the focal length of the lens used. At $\times 1$ the lens-film distance is doubled; hence this rule indicates that only one-fourth as much light actually gets from the lens to the film. If exposure time is to be kept within reasonable bounds one of two things must be done: (1) the diaphragm must be opened up two full stops over the calculated amount, or (2) the light falling on the subject must be correspondingly increased. But we have just seen that raising the magnification of the image also decreases, at any given f-stop, the depth of field. Therefore, if there is to be any significant amount of field-depth flexibility retained and the exposure time still kept within practical limits, one *must* raise the light level. It is by now obvious that by the time that the $\times 40$ to $\times 80$ range is reached the problem can reach formidable proportions, and time exposures (extending at times up to 30 to 60 seconds) will be the rule rather than the exception wherever practical.

A subsidiary problem in light falloff through magnification is that the ground glass image can become very dim, especially when the lens is stopped down to the working level. A magnifier of about ×6 to ×10 power is useful here, not only to check the accuracy of focus at the ground glass, but also to serve as a light gatherer and thus aid the eye in observing the degree of depth of field gained by stopping down.

As described earlier (and illustrated in Figure 7, p. 27), the simplest way to help matters is to use a high intensity source such as a spotlight, place it as close to the subject as is reasonably practical, place a hand magnifier before it to serve as an additional light beam concentrator, and then be *sure* to place a water cell between the lamp and the subject to cool the beam so that the subject will not suddenly shrivel and disappear in a little blue cloud of smoke. Even after these drastic steps, at extreme magnifications or with active subjects it may be necessary to use a faster film than desired. This will be especially likely if color film is being used, and fairly short exposures are needed to avoid color shifts due to reciprocity failure (see later section on Color, p. 65).

For concentration of light a handled magnifier can be used, with a common lab stand as a support. Or one of the readily available plastic fresnel lenses can be taped to the subject side of the water cell (it, too, may need protection from the heat). All necessary reflectors, diffusers, mirrors, and other equipment can be used with this high-intensity beam just as with less concentrated sources of light. It has been said that no use of light-concentrating lenses can increase the intensity of a light source. This is so. But such lenses can be used to cause the convergence of light rays that would otherwise have diverged. Thus there is made available for use light that would otherwise have been lost.

Calculation of exposure. Another difficulty now arises—that of calculating the correct exposure. The problem is twofold: (1) the light falloff inside the camera is not considered in the scale of the standard light meters, and (2) the sheer small size of the subject and the cramped nature of the setup may render normal measurements difficult or impossible by measuring systems using either reflected or incident light.

There is a standard formula for finding exposure increase needed at magnifications (exposure is first metered by normal means and the formula then applied to the results):

$$\text{effective f-value} = \frac{\text{indicated f-value} \times \text{lens-film distance}}{\text{focal length of lens used}}$$

or

$$\text{f-v}_{\text{eff}} = \frac{\text{f-v}_{\text{ind}} \times \text{d}_{\text{l-f}}}{\text{fl}}$$

Example: If f-v_{ind} is 22

d_{l-f} 15 inches

fl   5

then

$$\text{f-}v_{eff} = \frac{22 \times 15}{5} = 66$$

At a setting of f/22, assume that the effective f-value is f/64, which is the setting nearest the calculated f/66. Having used this formula, and having thereby found that, *in the example given*, the necessary exposure adjustment is three stops (f/22—32, 45, 64) there remains a choice. One can open up three stops— and thereby lose that much depth of field. Or, if the f/22 aperture is necessary, one can increase the exposure time by three stops. If this is to be the case, and assuming that the calculated exposure time was to be 4 seconds, the new exposure time will be 32 seconds (4 seconds—8, 16, and 32 seconds). And at this long exposure time reciprocity failure will enter, requiring a further exposure increase of perhaps one-third to one-half or more. In this hypothetical case a faster film might be desirable, or perhaps some further efforts at increasing light intensity.

The foregoing method of calculation of exposures is fine where the magnification is such as to allow normal methods of using a light meter to determine the exposure in the first place. For those who have suitable equipment and care to take the initial amount of trouble, however, there is a better and simpler means of exposure reading which removes all secondary calculations except that of possible additional time for reciprocity failure. This works by first calibrating the meter to the circumstances, but can only be successful with the most sensitive meters.

In this case the reading is taken directly from the image on the ground glass of the camera. (Larger cameras allow one to choose any desired portion of the subject to read on, but with 35-mm single-lens reflexes one must read the ground glass as a whole—a slightly less satisfactory means as it requires more judgment on the part of the worker.) Since, if the meter is sensitive enough, the reading can be taken after the diaphragm is stopped down to the operating aperture and even after any desired filter is in place, there will be only one variable to determine—the exposure time itself.

Calibration is achieved in the following way. A carefully standardized setup is made, and a meter reading is taken on a selected area of the image on the ground glass, this reading being recorded. Then a series of stepped exposures are made with the setup remaining unchanged. After development of the film the negatives are examined and the correct exposure time is keyed to the meter reading. As a check then, change the setup to new circumstances, read the now calibrated meter, expose and develop a film, and see how it comes out. For black-and-white films it is best to read the darkest significant part of the ground glass image. Using the same calibration with color reversal films it is best to read the lightest significant part of the image.

Example: Using a Gossen Lunasix meter, Model I, the meter is set to the correct film speed. Then the meter aperture, set for a reflection reading, is applied to the selected part of the ground glass image. Shield the meter to prevent stray light from affecting the accuracy. Now press the low-light-level button and hold it down about 10 seconds (to allow time for the needle to settle), release it to lock the needle, and see what you have. The needle reading is transferred to the circular slide rule of the meter in the normal manner. The correct exposure time will be found opposite f/1.4 on the scale. This f-reading will remain constant, since with the diaphragm already stopped down it is removed as a variable, the only remaining one being the exposure time, as noted above.

Any meter sensitive enough to show a significant swing of its needle at a ground glass reading under operating circumstances can be used.

Flash lighting. Where the use of flash is necessary when working at magnifications, some special problems arise. Two of these are owing to the probable necessity of placing the lamp or lamps closer than normal to the subject. The first of these is the sudden blast of heat released at the moment of the flash. A water cell between flash and subject may be needed to avoid overheating and possible destruction of the subject. Second, flash reflectors are designed to provide a certain type of beam at average distances. Used closer up, this beam pattern may be very different—perhaps distinctly uneven or not well related to the normal guide number. Use of reflectors and diffusers at the subject will even out the beam pattern, but testing to establish the guide number is a good idea.

A third difficulty may arise in the calculation of exposure even after testing of the guide number has been done. At magnifications it may be necessary to work at a given f-stop. Instead of calculating flash exposure by the normal formula (see p. 29), in which the f-value is the one variable, it may be desirable to use the formula to show the lamp-subject distance. With a known guide number and a certain f-stop (that is, the effective f-value not the indicated one—see formula, p. 47), we have the following:

$$\text{lamp-subject distance} = \frac{\text{guide number}}{\text{effective f-value}}$$

or

$$d_{\text{lp-sub}} = \frac{gn}{f\text{-}v_{\text{eff}}}$$

The procedure for calculating exposures or finding lamp-subject distances, then, is not particularly complex. However, it may be especially helpful if a chart of settings is precalculated and made up ready for use (see Appendix for a sample chart).

Control of movement and vibration. Another special difficulty in photography at magnifications is movement or vibration. A camera may be visualized as a sort of optical lever, with the subject at one end, the lens as the fulcrum, and the image as the other end. Under normal photographic conditions, the lens-image distance is very short compared to the lens-subject distance. Thus conditions are favorable. But at magnifications over $\times 1$ the situation is reversed. Consequently, movements of the subject or of the camera itself become greatly magnified in the image, because of the unfavorable "lever action." Such movements can be controlled in some cases, at least in part, by the use of short exposure times. In extreme cases only the use of electronic flash, with a flash duration of $1/1000$ second or less, will save the situation.

Where time exposures are needed—and this is of course where the subject moves not at all—it is of primary importance to see that all parts of the photographic setup are either very rigid or are not moved during the exposure. In extremely delicate cases, the shutter is not even used for fear of introducing vibration; it is kept open, and the exposure is timed by interrupting the light beam with a card. The workroom must be moderately darkened to prevent recording of stray light. Vibration, whether in the room itself or in the camera and its parts, is a great and common difficulty in this work, and all practical steps must be taken to avoid it and eliminate it. In areas where heavy motor traffic causes building vibration, it may even be necessary to work only during hours when traffic is lightest.

Indicators of scale. A final consideration in work at magnifications is the need for indicators of scale to be included in the picture. These are by no means always needed, but are often desirable—particularly where the final picture may end up reproduced unpredictably reduced or enlarged. The indicators of scale can either be photographed together with the subject (where they must be placed at the principal plane of focus to be accurate), or they may be added to the negative or print later. If photographed with the subject, they can be an actual scale—usually metric—or some common object of known and standard size. If the magnification is at all high, beware the use of actual scales, as they are seldom perfect enough to stand much enlargement without showing unpleasant irregularities in the graduations.

For high magnifications, adding the scale later is best. The work is done at a known degree of enlargement. A line of the correct length can then be scored or drawn on the negative; for $\times 40$, for instance, a line 40 mm in length will represent 1 mm. If the print background is to be black, the negative will be transparent there, and a line can be drawn on it with india ink or a narrow strip of opaque tape can be applied. In either case the result will be a white line on the print. If the background is to print white, it will be opaque in in the negative, and a knife point can be used to score a line in the emulsion. This will print black. Alternatively, suitable lines can simply be drawn on the final print itself.

7

FILTERS

The use of filters is widespread and necessary in scientific photography. Their purpose is to alter the nature of the light that forms the image. This is done by (1) selective color filtration, (2) polarization, or (3) reduction of intensity. A brief summary only will be given, as the subject is well covered elsewhere in a variety of sources. And the ideas involved are not in practice difficult to understand.

Filters come in several forms. They can be pieces of colored glass, the colors being produced as properties of the glass itself. These are durable, easily handled, and easily cleaned, but in some cases are subject to eventual fading or color change.

Filters can also be made by depositing a molecular film on one side of a sheet of clear glass. In this case the glass serves solely as a support for the molecular film, the purpose of the coating being usually to diminish the amount of light passed without otherwise altering it. These are called neutral-density filters, and they come in a variety of carefully graded and labeled densities. A beam-splitter mirror is also usually of this type of construction, the silvering or other reflective coating being just such a molecular deposit, but in some cases being colored (see Lighting for references to beam splitters). Neutral-density filters are without color effect (hence the word "neutral").

A third method of filter construction is to put a colored gelatine between two sheets of glass; the glass to support and protect the gelatine. Many high-quality color filters are made this way. Polarizing filters are often similarly constructed, with a sheet of polarizing material between two glasses.

Optically, the best type of filter is the unprotected gelatine itself. While subject to damage from scratching and finger marking, they are cheap enough to replace easily and to let one own a sizable variety. Being extremely thin, they are very good optically. Carefully handled, they can last a surprisingly long time. They can also, if need arises, be cut to special shapes and sizes with scissors. Polarizing material can also be had in sheets and rolls.

Glass or glass-mounted filters can have a very detrimental effect on image sharpness if they are of poor optical quality or if they are not accurately mounted at exact right angles to the optical axis of the camera. And neutral density filters, being usually primarily designed for use at the light source rather than at the lens, should be watched particularly closely for such defects. Final focusing with glass-mounted filters on cameras which allow ground glass viewing should be done with the filter in place, as they may make a slight difference in the focus. This is especially so if the filter is mounted inside the camera, as is commonly done with view cameras. In high magnification work it is best where practical to filter the light at its source rather than at the lens, in order to avoid any such difficulties.

Types of Filters

COLOR FILTERS

In black-and-white scientific photography there is frequently a need to differentiate colors which, when photographed on panchromatic films, will be reproduced as similar shades of gray because of their approximately equal brightnesses. In color differentiation on black-and-white films the need will be either to darken or lighten a given color relative to adjoining colors. The principle is simple: to darken a color, use a filter of complementary color; to lighten it, use one of the same color. Deeper or lighter hues of filters will provide correspondingly greater or less filter effect (see Figure 21). To observe the effect roughly as panchromatic film will record it, simply hold the chosen filter before your eye and look at the subject through it. You will see a monochromatic scene, with the relative brightnesses approximately similar to those of the final print. While it will be in shades of the color of the filter, rather than in shades of gray, as in the print, a very little practice will allow substantial prediction of final results by this method. Whole books can be and have been written about the use of color filters, but the essential practical principle is here described; such books serve only to elaborate and particularize it. (See Plate VI for examples of filtration effects.)

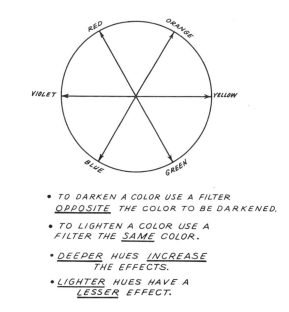

Figure 21. *Filter chart*

- TO DARKEN A COLOR USE A FILTER
  <u>OPPOSITE</u> THE COLOR TO BE DARKENED.

- TO LIGHTEN A COLOR USE A
  FILTER THE <u>SAME</u> COLOR.

- <u>DEEPER</u> HUES <u>INCREASE</u>
  THE EFFECTS.

- <u>LIGHTER</u> HUES HAVE A
  <u>LESSER</u> EFFECT.

 With color films, color filters are not used for the above purpose or by that method. Color differentiation is inherent in the film itself, and a color filter only imparts its own color to the entire image. Certain pale color filters do have uses in color photography, though, and will be separately discussed later (see section on Color).

POLARIZING FILTERS

 Polarization is one of the effects of the wave-action nature of light. Theory will not be discussed in detail but, briefly, it is sufficient to say that unpolarized light operates as waves in all planes about the axis of the light beam. A simple analogy would be a length of rope fastened at one end and handheld at the other. The rope represents the axis of a beam of light. By rapidly raising and lowering the rope end, a wave action is set up along its length. If this wave action is seen as taking place in all planes about the rope "beam axis," the analogy is complete. Polarized light operates as though the rope had been passed through a gap in a picket fence a foot or so from the held end. The wave action along the "beam axis" parallel to the gap in the fence would not be restricted, but this action could not be made to rotate about the axis of the "beam." The analogy here is oversimplified, but it seems adequate for under-standing.

There are three sources of polarized light that are photographically useful: (1) light from the clear blue sky, partially polarized through the scattering of direct sunlight from atmospheric particles, polarization being strongest at 90° from the position of the sun and zero in the direction of or opposite to the direction of the sun; (2) light which has been reflected from most types of non-metallic smooth surfaces, polarization being strongest at an angle of 35° from the reflecting surface and zero at 90° to it; and (3) light which has been passed through some form of polarizing material or device.

The filter material now most commonly used is Polaroid, produced by the firm of the same name. Its use is the only means of achieving polarization artificially that will be discussed here. (Polarizing methods using Nicol or Glen-Thompson prisms, tourmaline or other naturally polarizing minerals, bundles of obliquely placed glass plates, Nörremberg doublers, and others, are not in everyday photographic use; persons desiring information on such methods are referred to the Bibliography, especially to Strong.)

In practical application, polarizing filters can be used in three ways.

The first use applies to the polarized light that comes from the clear blue sky. A polarizing filter placed at the camera lens will, when rotated correctly, deepen the blue tones of the sky without altering other color values in the picture. The degree of deepening depends upon the angle of the sun's position with respect to the camera axis. The degree of effectiveness is also related to the degree of atmospheric clarity. Haze, by rescattering the light, may diminish the effect, although under some circumstances the haze obscuring distant land areas may itself be penetrated by the use of polarizers. The effect of sky-darkening (and of haze penetration) is useful in both color and black-and-white photography; it is indeed the only way by which skies can be darkened with color films. With black-and-white films the normal practice is to use yellow, orange, or red filters to darken skies, but there may be cases where this would result in unfortunate changes elsewhere in the picture area—for example, a red filter would darken the greens of the foliage as well as the blue of the sky. But a warning is in order when the polarizing filter is used, too: watch out for what effect the concomitant reduction of reflections may have on the rest of your picture.

The second use of polarized light is in the control and suppression of reflections from surfaces. A useful degree of control can be had by suitably rotating a polarizing filter at the camera lens if the camera axis is at an angle of about 35° to the reflecting surface. At this angle such reflections are most strongly polarized. At greater or lesser angles, suppression will be less complete but may still be useful. If, however, two surfaces at right angles to one another are both reflecting, this method can completely subdue only one of the reflections at a time. The plane of polarization of such reflections is parallel to the reflecting surface; hence two surfaces at 90° to one another, both at about 35° to the camera axis, will produce reflections whose polarization planes are oriented at 90° to one another. In such a case the best that can be done in an over-all way is equal partial suppression of both reflections.

If complete suppression of all reflections is desired, then the most practical approach is to use artificial light. Place a polarizing sheet before each light source, and put a polarizing filter on the lens of the camera. While observing through the lens filter (itself not to be rotated), have each lamp filter rotated until reflections disappear. Adjust each light separately, then turn it off while doing the next. Only when all the lamp polarizers are correctly positioned with respect to the lens filter will the effect be complete. Then all the lights being used can be turned on together, the exposure calculated (and don't forget filter factors), and the picture taken. In such a setup all the light striking the subject is already polarized, so the camera angle is immaterial to the result.

The third use of polarizing filters is to take advantage of the effects of polarized light on certain types of animal, mineral, and vegetable structures. This is the normal usage with mounted microscope slides viewed by transmitted light, but polarization effects in plastic materials or other suitable larger specimens can also be photographed by similar means. Briefly, the subject is placed between two polarizing filters. Different effects are achieved by rotating one of the filters or by rotating the subject between them.

When transmitted light is passed through polarizers in this manner, the light passage is unrestricted (except, of course, for the normal absorption of all waves not at the angle of polarization) so long as the two filters are at similar angles. However, when one filter is rotated with respect to the other, the light is gradually diminished until, at 90° rotation, very little light is passed at all. Reverting to our previous analogy, the effect is as though there were two layers to the picket fence. If one layer is rotated with respect to the other, the play of the rope "beam axis" will be gradually restricted until at 90° rotation, the rope passes through a simple hole and no waves are passed. Certain types of materials so affect the polarized beam passed by the first filter that some light is actually passed through the second filter, causing great visual changes in the image at the film plane. And, if the subject is at any stage rotated between the two filters, yet other visual effects take place. (For more detailed coverage of the physics of light in general and polarization in particular, see applicable references in the Bibliography, especially Strong and Drude.) For illustrations of polarization effects, see Plates IV, B and C; XIV, C; and XX.

NEUTRAL DENSITY FILTERS

Little discussion is needed here. As noted earlier, the function of this type of filter is solely to reduce light intensities. In the work discussed here, light more often needs increasing. But if these filters are used, they should be placed at the light source rather than at the lens. The risk of damage to the image sharpness is too great otherwise, since many neutral density filters are not designed to be used at the lens.

Filter Factors

Filters of all the types discussed act by removing some of the light. It is obvious, then, that if filters are used exposures must be increased to compensate for the loss. The amount of increase needed varies with the color and density of the filter. Standard tables of filter factors are available from filter manufacturers. Such information is also in part provided in the data sheet packed with each package of film. (Refer to the Bibliography for references giving further details on filters and filter factors.) It should be emphasized that the exposure increases to compensate for filtering are mandatory if under-exposure of films is to be avoided. And such underexposure can be very large; some filters can require increases as great as ten times the calculated exposure time.

8

REMOVING BONA FIDE ARTIFACTS

When it is of prime importance to present a piece of subject matter as clearly, succinctly, and unambiguously as possible, the intrusion into the picture of matter having no relationship to the subject is sometimes intolerable. Also to be avoided are marks and scratches produced by the circumstances of film use. There are a number of steps which can be taken more or less readily to remove such flaws from one's pictures.

Before considering removal of anything, however, the question which must first be decided is whether this removal is truly in the interests of scientific accuracy in presentation. In other words, is the material to be removed actually extraneous and unrelated? In most cases the answer will be obvious; sometimes it will not be so easy to decide where the limits lie. This section will attempt to provide some basis for judgment concerning these limits, as well as specific information on control of the situation.

It should be said at once that no change is the nature of the subject matter or of the resulting picture should ever be made which changes the character of what is being shown. Nor should any part of the photographic arrangement or technique itself intrude on the subject matter. The purpose of a science-oriented photograph is to record clearly and unambiguously what is there, and not to use the many and varied artifices of the field as a means of special pleading. No reputable scientist would do so intentionally, but there are times when enthusiasm and failure to consider the circumstances fully can lead one astray. Great care and considerable thought must be exercised in order to avoid unintentional misrepresentation.

Types and Techniques

DUST

Dust is the commonest contaminant in photography. Since it is airborne, it finds its way everywhere. It is, therefore, essential to clean the interiors and exteriors of cameras, film holders, enlargers, and all other equipment, frequently and thoroughly. Any speck of dust landing on a film prior to exposure throws a shadow during exposure, and leaves on the developed film a clear spot the size and shape of the original particle. This will print as a black speck or lint mark. If the dust mote lands on the negative before or during printing, it will produce, by the shadow it throws, a white spot on the print. And if the negative image is being enlarged, these spots will be similarly enlarged. These marks can be removed from both negatives and prints, but to do so is time-consuming and technically difficult to do well. Some such marks are inevitable and—to avoid any possibility of ambiguity—should be removed. But much grief can be avoided through simple cleanliness.

Another place to expect to find dust is on the subject matter itself, particularly where this subject is being magnified. Mounted insect specimens and other such materials that are kept for periods of time before photographing are unusually subject to gathering dust. Examination with a dissecting scope prior to photography will reveal their presence, and a light touch with a good watercolor brush will remove most such particles easily. Although seemingly an obvious point, the magnification of a subject to $\times 30$ or $\times 50$ will render a speck invisible to the unaided eye in truly heroic proportions (see Plate IX, C).

The presence of photographically undesirable dust can also be expected in culture media. Unless especially carefully prepared (with care beyond that needed for normal research purposes) nearly any agar or similar culture will have suspended in it and deposited on it minute particles of solid matter and lint. While this material may be sterile and biologically inert (or possibly even just some of the culture medium which didn't fully dissolve), it will be devastatingly visible if photographed by dark-field lighting, even at a mere $\times 1$. And for many purposes, such as the recording of precipitation bands, this sort of lighting is mandatory. A few minutes spent filtering a culture medium can save hours of retouching of prints later on. The moral is plain: if one is making cultures which will later be photographed, work carefully.

MARKS ON CONTAINERS

Marks on containers can cause aches in heads. In any case where the transparent container of photographic subject matter will come between subject and camera or will show beyond the subject (tube slants, petri dish cultures, plants grown in sterile tubes or flasks, and others), it is of course necessary to clean the exterior of the container before exposure.

Nor is dirt the only thing capable of disrupting the picture. Scratches and disfigurements in the glass itself can also disturb the view. In tubes and flasks this can best be controlled by selection of the glassware at the outset of the experiment. Petri dishes commonly become thoroughly scratched and abraded on their bottoms through repeated use. If cultures are destined for eventual photography, new dishes should be used, if practical. But this still leaves the matter of the concentric rings of uneven thickness and shape found on most petri dishes. If such rings are present or if the dish is scratched or abraded, all is not lost. Place a small quantity of clear, clean mineral oil on the glass supporting plate and float the dish on it. This will, through the similarity of its index of refraction to that of glass, effectively remove all such flaws from the picture. A bit messy, but very useful.

CONDENSATION ON GLASSWARE

Cultures or plant materials growing in contained environments present yet another problem—that of moisture condensing on the interior of the glassware and thereby partially obscuring and distorting the picture of the subject.

This is best countered by gentle warming of the container, which is readily done by putting an electric heating coil in a reflector and playing it over the container until the air inside warms slightly and absorbs the offending moisture. Care must be taken to avoid overheating, and thereby damaging, the culture material. All setup work and exposure calculation must be done prior to heating, since the picture must be made immediately upon the disappearance of the last traces of moisture. Prolonged heating may produce new condensation through increased metabolic activity of the plant material, and any heating at all, followed by subsequent cooling, will produce temporary condensation greater than was originally present. No delay can, therefore, be tolerated between end of heating and beginning of exposure, or you may find yourself suddenly worse off than originally. And a second chance, after recondensing occurs, may require the lapse of some little time.

RETOUCHING NEGATIVES AND PRINTS

Retouching is best approached through avoidance. In this manner time and effort can be saved and ethical questions sidestepped. Much retouching results from the intrusion into the picture of matter on the films, negatives, and subject material which ought not to have been there in the first place.

But there remain a few areas and categories where some handling will be necessary. With due regard to the principles and ethics mentioned earlier, we will discuss these and the techniques for taking care of them.

Dust on the subject matter and on films and negatives has already been discussed. Similar in principle to dust is water-borne contamination, which deposits particles during washing of both negatives and prints. Frequent cleaning of washers and the use of fully filtered water supplies will eliminate nearly all of this type of contamination.

Such contaminants are not the only things which must be removed from pictures in order to reproduce the subject clearly and unambiguously, however. Subjects immersed in liquids during photography may slough off pieces which scatter over what is intended to be a plain background, either black or white; a background may print as gray when white is needed; or it may later prove desirable to remove one of a group of articles in a picture for some legitimate reason. All of these circumstances will be discussed in the following paragraphs. It is obvious that working directly on negatives is practical only where the negative size is fairly large. Generally speaking, 35-mm negatives are too small to allow this sort of work.

If the background is intended to be white, or if there are extraneous objects on a white background, there is a simple way to get the desired result. Since a background that is to be white in the print is black on the negative (or near enough to call it so), the solution is to paint the desired areas of the negative black. This is done with a specially prepared mixture, available in photo stores, called "opaque." Care must be taken, of course, not to paint over the edge of the subject matter. In edging, a good method is to work with a magnifier and paint *not quite* to the edge. Then, if the background was not too dark to begin with, the remaining halo will probably not be visible to the viewer. If the background *was* too dark, then the edge must be very accurately delineated; this requires a steady hand. Extraneous objects are simply painted over. This use of opaque is called "blocking out" or "opaquing."

With backgrounds that are intended to be black on the prints (and are clear on the negative, or so light as to print as though clear), but where specks or objects intrude, there are two possible approaches. The most direct one is to use a knife edge to scrape the emulsion itself from the offending areas. The negative may look pretty bad at this time, but if the background will actually print black these marks will not show at all. The method works very well.

If a more subtle approach is desired, you can use a chemical reducer, such as some variation of the old reliable Farmer's Reducer (see Bibliography for sources on chemicals). A useful variation of this is to make up two stock solutions: one a saturated solution of sodium thiosulphate (hypo), and the other a saturated solution of potassium ferricyanide. To use, pour roughly equal amounts of both into a pan of water, and swab the resulting mixture onto the offending areas. Continued application will remove any amount of specks or blobs of a photographic nature from either negatives or prints. The working solution can be mixed to any degree of strength desired, though about 5–10% is usually about right. Accuracy of mixing is not essential, but print reduction (for removing dark areas from white backgrounds or even for lightening generally some areas of the subject itself—sparingly) normally requires a weaker mix than does negative work. Too strong a mix may produce a yellow stain on the print which may be hard to wash out.

After reduction, both negatives and prints should be stabilized by refixing and rewashing.

REMOVING SPOTS, SPECKS, AND SCRATCHES FROM NEGATIVES AND PRINTS

It will not be found possible to avoid entirely some dust and dust marks on negatives. There will also be occasional scratches found on important negatives. These and their resulting print blemishes can be removed through the use of one of the commercially available retouching and spotting compounds, which come either as liquids or as pigments deposited on a card. The liquid forms are used by brushing some of the liquid onto a small glass plate and allowing it to dry. This (or the dry pigment-on-card material) is then picked up in minute quantity on the tip of a finely pointed damp brush, and appropriately deposited on the negative or print. Spotting, as this is called, as well as other more complex forms of retouching, require skill for good results, and detailed instructions can not be given here. But the importance of spotting in cases where ambiguity can enter requires some discussion.

Enough skill at spotting to remedy most minor situations can be acquired through only moderate practice. For a beginner the dry-pigment type of spotting compound is the most practical, since it forms on the print only surface deposits, which can be readily removed in case of error. The liquid forms are usually dyes that penetrate the surface of the print. While more subtle and less visible, once applied they are essentially unremovable.

If a flaw in a negative results in a white mark on the print, it is best not to attempt to retouch the negative, as prints are easier to work on. Where the flaw will print black, the easiest solution for the inexperienced is to spot it so that it will print as a white speck and then retouch it out on the print. Unskilled negative retouching will show blatantly on the print, while satisfactory work can usually be done on the final print quite readily. And one's errors do not repeat on every print, as they do when retouching is on the negative.

Extensive retouching, as is commonly done by the more routine studio portraitists, is neither desirable nor ethically defensible in scientific work. Research reporting should be fact and not fiction. But in some cases it may help to darken or lighten an edge slightly to aid differentiation. It is not ethical to do so unless the exact position and shape of that edge is already visible enough to serve as a guide and is carefully maintained. Retouching should not be used as a late substitute for poor technique in lighting.

The actual technique is quite simple, though it requires some finesse in handling. Spots are darkened by using the tip of the spotting brush to deposit one or more tiny dark specks in the white area until it matches its surroundings. Scratch marks can be filled by doing this in row fashion, or by repeatedly stroking the exact scratch line with a very weakly charged brush. Edges are strengthened by the latter means. Lines are harder than spots, so practice a bit on nonessential prints before tackling an irreplaceable one. Overspotting is as bad as no spotting.

9

SPECIAL CONSIDERATIONS OF COLOR WORK

General Statement

In scientific research photography the main uses of color films are to produce projection slides for use in classes or meetings, and to produce original color illustrations to be used in journal or book illustration. Although there will be no special discussion of projection slides, much of what will be said applies to them, too. The cost of color reproduction keeps its use in journals relatively rare, but since it does occur some discussion is appropriate.

It is possible to use either positive or negative materials in color photography, and for publication purposes either can be successful. But for technical reasons the use of positive color transparencies is usually to be preferred. Transparency work is simpler for most users because the accuracy of color reproduction is determined largely at the time of the original exposure, by using films matched to the light sources used, by correcting with suitable filters any slight maladjustments of either film color accuracy or color temperature of the lamps, and by using care in obtaining correct exposures. With color negative films, the correction of color is done at the time of printing, and is more likely to be off color than on. Correcting it can be a difficult and time-consuming process, particularly if great accuracy in color is desired and if at the time of printing one does not have the original subject present for matching purposes. If commercially done, exact color matching is very expensive.

Really exact matches of colors are rare and quite unlikely, since the dyes presently used and available to the industry are not ideal spectrally. However, a very satisfactory job can be done if suitable precautions are taken at the outset. Color balances vary among the different makes of film and, to some extent, among different batches of the same film. This is especially apparent when paired comparisons are made of similar subject matter, or when a continuing job is split between two batches of film. It is, then, desirable to buy color film in moderately large lots (all of the same emulsion number), test the initial rolls or sheets under controlled circumstances to determine if and what correction filters will be needed, and then use the remainder under similarly controlled circumstances. Only in this way can consistently comparable results be obtained.

Reciprocity failure should be mentioned here. In black-and-white films this effect requires for its correction only some additional exposure. In color films it will be found that the emulsion is multilayered to record all the colors and that—owing to the structure of this layering—the different layers will be differently affected by reciprocity failure. The result of this differential reciprocity failure will be that excessively long or short exposures may produce more or less pronounced color shifts, as well as the familiar underexposure effect (see section on Basic Photography). At the expense of adding even more exposure time, these color shifts may be corrected through the use of color correction filters. In some cases the color shifts can not be corrected. Film data sheets should be checked for information on this subject prior to use. Where the manufacturer says that some procedure is "not recommended," the usual meaning is that the procedure will produce a noncorrectible color shift. This matter may be very important in such uses as work at high magnifications, where light falloff through bellows extension is present.

For high-quality color reproduction it is necessary to employ the sharpest, finest-grained materials that can be used in the given circumstances. For 35-mm cameras the standard for judgment is, and has been since its original introduction, Kodachrome. Circumstances may require the use of other films, but this will usually result in larger grain, less sharpness, less standardized processing, less accurate color rendering, or some combination of these. These factors vary from film to film, from great differences to minor ones. So the needs of the given case must govern the choice. For larger-sized cameras, Kodachrome is not available, so the use of other films is mandatory. On any large, important, or unusual project, check the manufacturers' claims well before standardizing on a film, both for accuracy and for suitability to the job at hand. For large camera use, the current best choices are probably Ektachrome E-3 for color accuracy, or Ektachrome-X for sharpness, good contrast, and brilliance of colors. With changing technologies these recommendations may be short-lived, but they stand at present.

In any event, excepting the single case of Kodachrome II, which is really exceptional in performance for most uses, the matter of best quality will usually be best served by using the largest films one has the equipment to handle. With large film sizes, and suitable testing and correction as described earlier, it will be found possible to obtain publication-grade results with any of the commonly available types and makes, except where special circumstances require use of a film having matching specific qualities. For such special cases consultation with the manufacturers' representatives is suggested.

In either large or small sizes the best accuracy in color exposures is obtained by "straddling" with three or more exposures, the central one at the calculated setting, and the others 1/3 to 1/2 stop to either side. It costs in terms of materials, but can be well worth it where ultimate quality is desired and the chance to repeat is not easily assured. And in 35 mm the additional cost is usually negligible (see frontispiece and Plate VII for color photos).

Backgrounds

In color work, backgrounds present more different possibilities than they do in black-and-white; it is possible to have them in any color desired, as well as black, white, or gray. Many writers on color photography for informational purposes suggest brightly colored backgrounds to take advantage of the visual attraction of sheer color. For scientific purposes, however, this seems less desirable, the main reason being that here it is usually important to preserve as much accuracy as is possible in the subject colors. And there is a peculiar psychological process which tends to cause an effect of color tinging to transfer from background to the subject where the former is the more highly colored. No actual transfer takes place in most cases, although in at least the earlier stages of a recently developed color printing process there seemed to be a tendency for the entire print actually to assume a tint from the dominant color in the picture area. That there is usually no actual transfer can be determined experimentally, but the eye tends to see it as though it exists. The only situation where actual color transfer takes place with any and all films is where light reflects obliquely onto the subject from an overlarge background or from other colored objects in the vicinity.

What then is the most desirable background color for scientific reporting? As in most other matters discussed here, "it all depends." For some uses colors are quite permissible, usually where a natural or seminatural effect is being attempted; for example, a light blue card placed behind a twig or leaf grouping will simulate a sky tone. But most often backgrounds should be in neutral tones.

For subjects where a dramatic effect is desired and particularly where it is desirable to call attention to subtle pastels, the best background color is black—preferably the absolute black produced by using deep-pile velvet as a backing. The blackness of the background forces the viewer's attention upon the subject and, by its own total lack of color, makes it more likely that the eye will perceive all of the subject's subtleties.

Some workers may prefer a more understated approach, just as some subjects may benefit from it, especially those which are themselves brightly colored. In this case a plain white backing is useful; but if the photograph is intended for projection, beware a *too* white background, which will produce too much glare. A *very* light gray or just a slight trace of a suitable color may be preferable. Darker grays and darker shades of the more muted colors are appropriate where the subject is very light but where black backgrounds are undesirable or tend to create ambiguity.

Lighting

Standard texts on color photography often remark that lighting contrasts should be less than for black-and-white photography. In actual practice—particularly where the use will be projection rather than publication—it will be found that one can get away with contrasts that would be hopeless in black-and-white. Why? Because in color work one can readily distinguish variations in shadow and highlight from color differences.

A fairly safe generalization, according to the techniques described earlier for scientific photography, is that informationally suitable lighting for black-and-white use will also produce good results in color. The reverse is not necessarily true. A type of lighting that produces a quite acceptable color slide may reproduce execrably in black-and-white or even in printed color. This point is well worth noting by those who primarily use color slide materials but may wish later to convert them to black-and-white for publication (of which, more later in Copying).

Filters

As mentioned earlier, the colored filters normally used with black-and-white films cannot be used with color films, since they will simply produce an over-all color cast of their own hue. With color films the use of color filters is restricted to those very pale ones designed to correct imbalances in films or in color temperatures of lamps.

All color transparency films are designed to be used with light sources that are calibrated for color balance in terms of "color temperature," measured in degrees Kelvin (for sources giving further discussion of this system, see Bibliography). This is the basic difference between Daylight, Tungsten, and Flash color films. Cross use can be made through the use of color correction filters; the necessary information for this is given in the data sheets packed with the film. For accurate color rendition, then, one should use a film suited to the light source or filtered for correction to it. And one cannot mix light of two different color temperatures (say, daylight and tungsten sources) in one picture without badly upsetting the results.

Color photography by the light of fluorescent lamps is to be avoided where possible. These lamps are different from sunlight and incandescent lamps in that they have no true color temperature; their radiant energy is produced by a different means. Color films, being calibrated to true color temperature, will yield unpredictable responses. Lists of filter corrections for various fluorescent lamps are available (see Bibliography), but it should be understood that their use requires testing under actual working conditions and can still not guarantee optimum results. Fluorescent lighting may in some circumstances be necessary, but for color work it is never preferred.

Polarizing filters retain their properties in color use. They are normally gray in color, and so impart no color casts. One primary use is that of deepening sky color without affecting subject color except in that surface reflections may be eliminated and surface color thereby deepened. There is no other way of achieving a darkened sky with color films. Polarizing filters are otherwise used the same as with black-and-white films for reflection control and for any other control and use of polarized light and polarizable subject matter.

Neutral density filters, being neutral in color, are used without change with either black-and-white or color films.

Filter factors apply with color films just as they do with black-and-white, including color correction filters. Charts for such use are available from suppliers.

PART
III

Solutions to Problems

10

GENERALIZED PROBLEMS

Control of Reflections

One of the most common difficulties in scientific photography is the unwanted presence of reflections of the lights, either on the subject itself, on its container, or on a surface between the subject and the camera. Such reflections can nearly always be eliminated or substantially reduced by one means or another.

The quickest and easiest method of controlling a reflection is by moving the light or lights until—from the camera position—the reflection is either subdued or entirely gone. This works best in cases where the reflection is on a flat surface—a piece of sheet metal, a glass case enclosing the subject, or other such surface. The positional change needed is usually not great. The original presence of the reflection arises from having failed to fully realize the implications of the laws of reflection.

Since the angle of reflection equals the angle of incidence, certain lamp placements, as in Figure 22, A, will result in a reflection. Moving the lamp, as in Figure 22, B, will correct matters.

If the surface showing the reflection is irregular in shape, and changing the positions of the lamps serves only to move the reflection around, a suitable method of control—if the subject will not be damaged—is to immerse it in liquid. Useful liquids are distilled water (distilled to reduce the annoyance of air bubbles present in freshly drawn tap water), alcohol in various dilutions

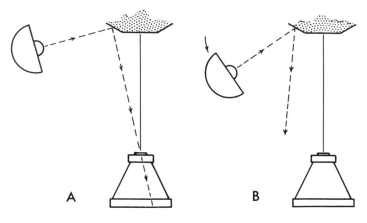

Figure 22. *Control of reflections*

according to the subject, glycerin (though subject to visible striations due to varying density), and mineral oil. This last is very useful with insects embedded in amber, owing to the similarity of index of refraction, which not only cuts out surface reflections but also reduces distortions introduced by irregularities in the shape of the amber. The effect of liquid immersion is to ensure that the only surface producing direct reflections of the lights is the liquid surface itself, which, being flat, can be readily controlled by the placement of the lamps.

If liquid immersion is impractical and the lights cannot be moved about (or such movement does not suffice), there still remains a good solution—the use of polarizers (as described earlier under Filters). The main difficulty here arises through a severe loss of light, necessitating an increase in exposure time. Where a setup is employed with incandescent light sources polarized with filters, and with a polarizing filter at the camera lens, the exposure increase needed is about five times (see Plate XX).

A secondary source of reflection difficulty, after all light source reflections have been controlled, comes in cases where some flat surface lies between camera and subject and is perpendicular to the optical axis. This can be a glass cover, the surface of the immersing liquid, and so on. The difficulty arises from the reflection of the camera or lens mount and shows up in the center of the picture area. This can usually be removed by putting the camera behind a screen of black paper or other material, with a hole cut out for the lens. This type of reflection is easily missed when setting up the picture but is very disturbing in the final picture; watch for it carefully.

Control of Movement

Where fine detail is essential, as in scientific photography generally, the danger of loss of sharpness from camera movement can scarcely be overestimated. In nearly all cases where the camera is hand-held, the limiting factor in resolving fine detail lies not in the capabilities of the lens or film, but rather in the amount of camera motion at the moment of exposure. It is only when exposures are shorter than about 1/250 to 1/500 of a second that really sharp pictures can be taken with a hand-held camera—other than through chance momentary stillness at the exposure interval. The *full* resolution potential of either camera or film can only be realized when the camera is firmly supported. The individual worker must determine for himself—preferably through comparison trials—when and where he can afford to do hand-held work. That is, when and where the mobility is more important than sharpness; when and where the needed degree of sharpness becomes impractical without a support (see earlier remarks under Choice of Equipment, p. 11).

Motion of the subject itself is another source of difficulty, though more obvious than camera movement.

Both types of motion can be minimized by the use of high shutter speed or by using a high-speed flash unit as the exposure device. And both of these methods of control can be assisted by using one of the very fast films currently available.

If for some reason it becomes desirable with live subject matter to use time exposures—if, for instance, the exact lighting setup is critical and makes flash use questionable, and great depth of field is necessary—other methods may be used. Most organisms have moments or even considerable periods of natural quietude; even 20- or 30-second exposures can readily be made of many types of insects, if care is taken. In extreme cases, the subject can of course be anesthetized. This is quite practicable where only the form and not the habits of the subject is of importance.

The method used to minimize the effects of camera or subject movement is not in itself important. The great thing is to realize the need or desirability of doing so, and then devise a means suitable to the task.

Rendering Spherical and Cylindrical Objects

For the beginner attempting careful lighting, one of the more elusive goals is the satisfactory illumination of spherical and cylindrical subject matter. It is hard to show the shape without at the same time obscuring some of the detail.

For spherical objects a good method of lighting is to use a variation of the reflector-diffuser setup described earlier under Lighting. In this case the reflector and the diffuser together completely surround the object, while close to it, inside the reflector-diffuser ring, is placed a ring of black paper which rises to about the midline of the subject. Correctly placed (see Figure 23) the result is a slight soft shadowing completely around the perimeter of the subject, which clearly indicates the shape without being so strong as to conceal any sort of detail (Plate VIII, A and B).

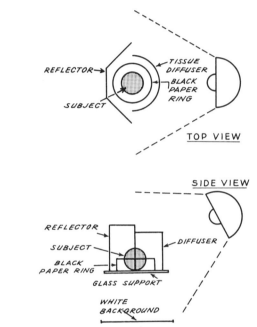

Figure 23. *Lighting spheres*

Cylindrical objects, to provide maximum information content in the photograph, preferably are lit from the end, either by direct or diffused light. Cross lighting makes shadow control difficult, and definition of the edge nearest the light is difficult to differentiate against a light or white background. With black backgrounds, of course, it would be the edge *away* from the light that would tend to blend with the background. An exception might arise in the case of a metallic object, where drama of presentation is more important than detail within the object (Plate VIII, C and D).

With both spheres and cylinders it may once in a while help the showing of shape to place a single specular highlight somewhere on it. More than one, however, tends to confuse the directionality of the lighting.

Showing Hairs and Hairlike Processes

One of the commoner attributes of living objects, whether plant or animal, is the presence of hairs or hairlike processes, either at edges or on the surfaces. Showing these well in a photograph can present a considerable problem to the inexperienced.

Perhaps the best way of showing such structures along edges is to use the dark-field lighting methods shown in Figures 16 and 17. With care it will be found possible to balance exactly this backlighting with ordinary top and frontal lighting, so that surface appearance can be shown at the same time (Plate V). If only top light is used, the edge hairs will usually not show against a black background, but the addition of the dark-field lighting will show edge hairs brilliantly. White backgrounds, when diffuse, tend to obscure edge hairs. Successfully showing such edge effects against white backgrounds usually requires an aligned beam such as is used in transmitted-light microscopy.

Surface hairs are usually best shown by throwing a direct light beam at a grazing angle across the subject (see Plate IX, A and B).

Showing Black Objects

Showing objects which are of an over-all dull black coloration requires printing them as gray. Best appearance is achieved usually by lighting diffusely and then printing to rather high contrast in tones up to dark grays. Moderate overexposure of the negative may help to increase the contrasts, by getting the dark main subject onto the middle, highest contrast, portion of the negative's tonal scale.

Shiny black objects will not appear to be shiny unless a specular reflection is left somewhere on them. Thus, a direct main light source is usually desirable. In some cases it may not be practical to use a reflector at all, since it may result in a large disturbing diffuse highlight on one side of the subject. Again, printing in terms of grays may be indicated, except that the very darkest areas should be just about black. Polarization may sometimes help. Only experimentation with particular subjects will tell.

In this day of "black boxes" for electronics and related pursuits, an increasingly common type of subject is a box or chassis painted dull black, and either wired with white-insulated wiring or accompanied with brightly polished fixtures. To show all these features well it is advisable to light at roughly normal contrasts, overexpose about two full stops, and develop normally (that is, without compensation for the overexposure). The result will be a very dense negative having relatively high contrasts in the shadow areas (the black box), and relatively low contrasts in the highlight areas (the white wires and the shiny chrome). A negative of this nature will be difficult or impossible to enlarge—exposure time in printing would be enormous—but contact printing is perfectly practical. And such a contact print will yield results that cannot be approached by any other means known to me. Because of the difficulty of enlarging, a large negative is, of course, necessary.

Showing Monochromatic Colorations

Although three-dimensional objects can be clearly shown through light and shadow, and multicolored objects can be differentiated through the use of color filters, there remains one type of subject that can be difficult to handle in black-and-white and sometimes even in color—a plant or mineral specimen which is primarily composed of areas of various shadings of essentially the same color.

In such cases the usual best approach is to light as low in contrast as possible, so that shape and surface texture are diminished to the vanishing point (through light tenting), and then print to high contrast.

Where this treatment is still not sufficient, and where no damage will result, immersion of the subject in distilled water will often greatly increase color contrasts. Mineral specimens will often exude trapped air in bubbles for some time after immersion, but these can usually be brushed off with a watercolor brush (see Plate IX, C and D).

11

SPECIFIC SUBJECT MATTER

The foregoing general coverages of the principles of photographic usage are useful for wide applications, and a knowledge of them will be assumed here, but some discussion of particular types of subject matter is called for. Relatively minor changes in some of the general setups can make some quite large differences, and it is not always obvious just which general technique will be most applicable in a given situation. Without some advance hint it may be difficult to determine just where to start and what changes may need to be made. Although particular types of subject matter will be described here, it should be realized that similar techniques may well be nicely applicable to quite different materials. And the described methods may not always be the correct or most applicable solution for some specimens within some of the classes of subject matter covered.

Techniques

APPARATUS AND LABORATORY EQUIPMENT

This category, being as it is so extremely varied in nature, involves some unusually difficult lighting situations, in many cases complicated by the presence of seemingly mutually exclusive—from a lighting standpoint—components. Discussions will necessarily be quite general.

Metal objects can be lit either by the normal direct and diffuse lighting techniques applicable to any three-dimensional object, or they can be lit by taking advantage of reflection principles. If the primarily important elements of a piece of apparatus or a laboratory setup are irregular in shape, the normal methods are usually far the best. If the surfaces are shiny and this shine tends to obscure detail, the probable best solution is extremely diffuse light, even to the point of light tenting.

Where the primarily important elements are largely composed of flat surfaces, bare metal or painted, then one can use the qualities of reflectivity of those surfaces (even if any painting is flat black). Here first choose a camera angle which best shows what is desired, then place a light on one side of the subject at the same angle as but in the opposite direction from the subject plane as the camera. This lamp will here be called the "reflectivity lamp," and will cause the surface detail to be very plainly shown, whether its texture is rough or smooth, dull or shiny, its color dark or light (see Figure 24 and Plate X). A fill lamp will usually be required to generally light the rest of the subject, and this should usually be placed on the camera side of the subject and close to the optical axis, to provide direct frontal lighting and thus maximum light with minimum shadowing. A third lamp may be required to light a background.

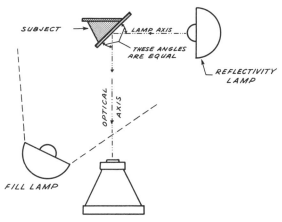

Figure 24. *Reflectivity lighting for apparatus*

Either or both of the two main lamps may have to be diffused. Cavities in the faces of such subjects may require yet another lamp to show their interiors. This may be a ringlight surrounding the lens, or more likely a small spotlight (even an ordinary flashlight in some cases) placed very close to the camera and adjusted for distance until its light level balances with the over-all level while penetrating the cavity. This kind of work requires close reasoning and lots of experimentation.

Glass. Most discussions of the photography of glassware show how to make the glass as conspicuous and glamorous as is possible. If this effect is needed, it can usually be achieved by using a black background and lighting from the edges all around or from such particular directions as best delineate the subject.

The commonest need in scientific work, however, is for lighting that will indicate the presence of the glassware while rendering it inconspicuous and suitably lighting the contents. Lab glass is mainly of importance as a container. Such lighting can use either black or white backgrounds.

With a black background, the usual method will be to light the subject from above with a direct lamp. With the proper setup the glass container will now be virtually invisible. Then, white cards, usually quite narrow in shape, are so placed at either side that they reflect from and indicate the shape of the outline of the container. They also serve, if correctly placed, to fill in by reflection the shadows of the main subject (see Figure 25).

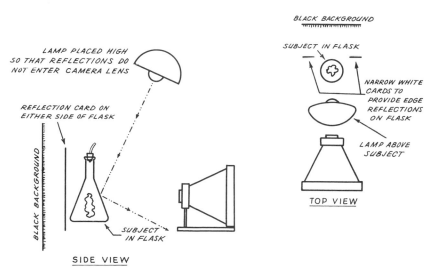

Figure 25. *Lighting subjects in glass containers*

With white backgrounds the situation is similar, except that the background may need a separate and brighter light, the background should be quite large for the size of the subject matter, and the edge reflection cards should be black instead of white. The result will be to show the whole container as an even, very light gray, which the black cards will provide with a thin black outline.

In some cases it may help to block out backgrounds very carefully on the negative so as to render the background pure white and thereby show up the light gray glassware better (Plate XVIII).

Electronic complexes are an increasingly common type of equipment subject. Panel faces, boxed components, and printed circuits can readily be handled by the methods described earlier in this section. In the earlier section on General Problems will be found a coverage of Black Objects. But clearly showing wired circuitry sometimes presents special problems, particularly in shadow control.

The great difficulty is to show clearly all wires, connections, and all of the myriad electronic parts which make up modern circuitry, without ambiguity and confusing shadows. This can usually best be done by placing one or another of the available types of ringlights before and surrounding the camera lens. If a great deal of this kind of work is contemplated, there is available a specially designed cold-cathode-tube lighting device which is really excellent, though rather expensive (the Hinelight Model B). Considerably less expensive and still quite effective lighting units can be built by combining the large, medium, and small fluorescent ringlights (8-, 12-, and 16-inch Circline lamps), commercially available at any good electrical shop, into one concentrically mounted unit. Electronic flash ringlights can be used with the smaller types of subject, but they are less useful with larger subjects.

Either of these two lighting setups combines several functions: (1) it penetrates cavities, (2) it lights flat plates perpendicular to the optical axis by reflection, and (3) it greatly minimizes or entirely does away with shadows of the individual wires and components.

If color work in large quantities is intended, the fluorescent fixture is less appropriate. The Hinelight mentioned above is best here since it is designed to produce light of the correct color temperature. (See earlier section on Color for further explanation; see Bibliography for suggested correction filtration for fluorescents, if their use is preferred.)

More complex types of subject matter may, as previously indicated, have all of these types of construction located within them. One can either light the whole works according to the needs of the single most important feature, arrange a compromise type of lighting which yields tolerable rendition of several areas, or try to light each component separately; this last can become difficult, if the end result is not to present a most peculiarly heterogeneous appearance. The demands of the situation dictate what will be done. In cases of really unusual complexity, it may be best simply to diagram the setup, and use photographs to provide detailed coverage of vital portions. The great variety of possible subjects makes more detailed discussion impractical.

ART OBJECTS AND ANTHROPOLOGICAL ARTIFACTS

Coins and medallions and other such objects can be lit by a variety of means. An easy and quick means of making photographs of large numbers of coins, while retaining a high degree of legibility of appearance, is to use a fluorescent ringlight around the lens, with a group of coins laid directly on an aluminum-foil background, as described earlier (see Figure 6). Since not all coins have the same degree of reflectivity, it may be necessary to print to several densities in order to display properly all the coins in a group. Grouping by surface appearance can aid one here. If differential printing is needed, it can be done either by cutting out suitable prints from sheets printed at various levels, or it can be done all on one sheet of paper by using printing masks to vary the exposure time given to the various coins—tedious in some cases, but very effective (see Plate XI, A).

For ultimate quality in coin and medallion photography there is a better method involving, usually, photographing one coin at a time. The coin is placed beneath a vertically mounted camera on a sheet of glass supported above the usual white card background. Diffuse window light is used to light the coin, which is turned to it for best lighting of portrait heads or other detail, and the background is separately lit by a beam of artificial light in sufficient strength to render it pure white in the final print. A reflector may or may not be needed at the subject level to fill the shadow areas (see Figure 26). It is important to determine the correct orientation of the coin or medallion and then light so that the relief work appears to be lit from the top left, top, or top

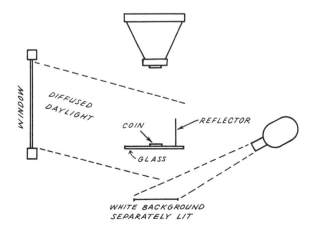

Figure 26. *Lighting a coin by window light*

right. If the lighting comes from below the relief may appear to be reversed.

Extremely low relief can be shown best, particularly on very dark subjects, by the use of a beam splitter, as earlier described in Lighting (see Plate XI, B).

Paintings and other flat artwork, including etchings, engravings, and so on, can usually be done readily with normal copy lighting (see later section on Copying). Paintings, for black-and-white reproduction, are done on panchromatic film in order to retain a scale of relative brilliances close to that of the eye. In either color or black-and-white, shiny surface reflections and hazes can be removed completely through the use of polarizing filters, as described earlier under Filters, and later under Copying. Paintings which are very large but still transportable can be evenly lit most easily by photographing them in direct sunlight. Polarizing filters are of little use in direct sunlight unless the surface of the painting is heavily convoluted, and polarized reflections may yield in part to a suitably rotated filter at the camera lens. Detailed coverage of such specialized techniques as ultraviolet photography of paintings can be found in the literature (see Bibliography).

Engravings, etchings, and lithographs are usually best photographed on one of the continuous-tone copy films, although in some cases, particularly woodcuts and the like, high-contrast "lith" films give either better reproduction or a chance for cheaper linecut reproduction (see Copying, later).

Points and other tools made of chipped stone usually require a relatively low-angled, grazing, direct light to show the work marks. Fill-in reflection should be minimal, only sufficient to provide some shadow detail. The direction of the light should be from just to one side of the pointed end (or picture top, if there is no point), as this usually best indicates relief as well as being a visually satisfactory orientation.

Polished tools, whether stone or bone, are well shown with diffused light directed along their longitudinal axes, and with rather high-contrast printing to indicate their shapes better. This is particularly true of pieces bearing incised designs that have been blackened for visibility by their makers.

Backgrounds in both of these lighting arrangements should generally be white—though bone shows well against black—and may require separate lighting to clearly delineate light-colored objects.

Pottery and other dishware. Vases and the like can be approached either as sculpture (see below) or as a special form of copy. For research purposes the latter method is more common. The aim is to show form and the nature of exterior decorations in complete detail, rather than to produce a glamour photo.

The setup uses two undiffused lamps, at about 45° to the optical axis on either side, with polarizers to remove the nearly inevitable crescent-shaped reflections. The background is usually white and is lit separately so as to print white. It should not be overly large, or it may introduce nonfilterable reflections on the sides of the vase. Background brightness should be carefully gauged, as blocking out on the negative is frowned on here. The exact outline is too important to chance an error in outlining. The lens should be of the longest available focal length to provide the best perspective and truest picture of the outline (see Figure 20). The lens also carries a polarizer.

Dishware of pottery or stone can be well photographed from directly above. A ringlight surrounding the lens will give good penetration of deeply dished items, and will also show comparative amounts of dishing in adjacent pieces (see Plate XI, C). The background should be a white card placed directly under the dishes, without any intervening space. With all but the very lightest of such subjects it will print as pure white. Very light subjects can be done against black velvet or, if white backgrounds are needed, they can be photographed separately, being placed directly on a sheet of aluminum foil, as in Figure 6 (p. 22).

Sculpture is usually approached much like portraiture. The desire of the photographer is to show the largest possible amount of individual character in the piece, along with the best possible feeling of the design motif. Lighting, then, is for shape and texture. For small pieces or large I prefer a single moderately diffuse source such as window light, directional but not harsh, with such reflector fill as is needed or desired (sometimes none, depending upon the subject). By moving the subject, the light source, or the camera—together or separately—you can achieve virtually any effect desired. (With subjects too large to move, the alternatives are of course reduced.) Complex lighting setups usually serve only to confuse the appearance of the photograph, while simultaneously draining out much of the force and import of the shapes. There are, of course, exceptions to the above, and there are those, too, who reject the whole idea of simple diffuse lighting for sculpture. Personal preference rules in this matter.

Direct frontal lighting, as with on-camera flash, is nearly always about the very poorest approach possible for portraying sculpture. The effect is to flatten relief, diminish surface textures, and generally bore the eye. These remarks also apply, of course, to pictures of people made this way.

Porcelains will be unusually well portrayed by ordinary window light or by some other well-diffused, single light source. The soft diffuseness will impart excellent modeling without allowing harsh highlights. Marbles and other stone works may benefit from more strongly directed sources such as undiffused floodlights. Metal work may require either of these, combinations of both, or lighting as prescribed for Metal (p. 77). No pat answers can be given for any case where the notion of art prevails. Final decisions rest on matters of esthetics and not on scientifically controlled circumstances (see Plates XII and XIII).

BOTANICAL SUBJECTS

Plant materials suitable for studio photography are of three main types: (1) whole potted plants, (2) leaves, stems, or other portions of plants, usually essentially alive and cut immediately before photography, and (3) mounted herbarium sheets. (Dish and other special cultures are described elsewhere; see p. 90.) The most common objectives are to show comparative size; attitude of the leaves on whole plants; color differences such as lesions, spotting from disease, insect damage, and so on; shape and texture abnormalities in diseased leaves; and typical characteristics of type specimens. Color differences are enhanced by suitable color filtering (if the colors to be shown are different). Water immersion of leaves or other plant portions may also be necessary if very shiny surfaces are present or if color differences are a matter of different shades of the same color. These matters have all been thoroughly covered earlier (pp. 70 and 75).

Potted plants. The usual points of importance in photographing potted plants are to show the general appearance and attitude of the plants, to indicate size and color, and to make comparisons of vigor. The simplest setup is to use a horizontally mounted camera, two lamps set at about 30–45° off the optical axis and to either side, and about 30–45° above it, pointing down at the subject. Diffusing screens will often be placed before the lamps. The camera is aimed either straight in or pointed slightly downward at the plant. In some few cases, plants are photographed at sharp angles downward, or even from directly above. Here it usually suffices to place one lamp, well diffused, on either side of the plant and pointing down at it at about a 45° angle. Difficulties are rather rare once the requirements of the situation are clearly in mind.

Backgrounds are usually white, since most plants are too dark to show well against a black background. Where the camera points directly or nearly directly downward, the handling is as described earlier for reflector-diffuser lighting, with the plant set on a glass support, with a directly lit white card below.

For horizontally arranged setups there is a method which results in a background either white or just slightly off-white, which is nearly always satisfactory. A curved white card is used as both base and background, and the pot is set, well forward, directly on it (Figure 27). In most cases the light on both plant and background is softly diffused, so that only the slightest shadowing is visible at the base of the pot. Care must be taken to assure that the background is evenly lit, and that the plant is suitably lit at the same time. If it is not possible to do both, put major attention on the plant and block out the background with opaque on the negative.

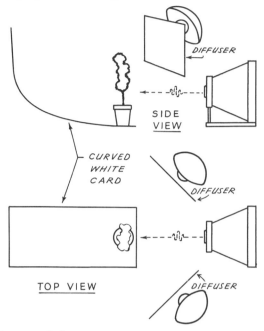

Figure 27. *Lighting potted plants*

Leaves and plant parts. A very common botanical subject is one or more leaves laid flat to show color and shape differences or abnormalities. The setup is as for normal reflector-diffuser lighting. Filters are frequently needed to show color effects (see Plates III, C, VI, and VII, A). Correct orientation is to consider the tip of the leaf the top of the picture and the petiole the bottom. Lighting is from the tip end. Relative positions of reflectors and diffusers can be varied to show any degree of surface modeling desired (see Plates III, C, and IX, B).

A variation is to show such a leaf by transmitted light only, in order to show better the internal structures and abnormalities. Lighting is as previously described under diffuse transmitted light. Filters can still be used.

The most common difficulties with leaf pictures are (1) accidental, too-strong background lighting, which results in flare around and through the leaf and loss of over-all contrast (similar results come from too large white backgrounds), and (2) surface shine from waxy leaves. Reduce background light strength (or background size) to eliminate the first difficulty; immerse in water to correct the second.

If leaves curl and refuse to lie flat, one solution is to wait until wilt just begins, before photography. Most leaves will then lie quite flat. Do not let them wilt too much, or changes in appearance will take place. Stubborn cases can often be made to lie quite flat by placing a sheet of glass on them. But one must watch out for reflections.

Stems and cut-off sections of stems showing lesions or other discoloration are another common type of botanical subject matter. These are lit similarly to leaves; the orientation is proper when the root end of the stem is to the bottom of the picture, with the light from the upper or leaf end. This results in correct lighting for cylindrical objects, that is, from the end. If such subjects are crosslit, there arises considerable difficulty in controlling contrasts, the side nearest the light being much too light. Much more even lighting and hence clearer rendition of detail is had by end lighting.

There may be need to dissect, lay out, and photograph the various parts of a flower. There is a combination lighting method which works very well for this. The subject parts are laid out correctly on a glass support, beneath which is placed a suitably sized fluorescent ringlight. The center of this light is filled in with black velvet, which is shaded from the light of the ring by a standing circle of black paper. Then pieces of black paper are laid flat on the glass support to surround the subject and thereby cut off from the lens the direct light of the ringlight. The result so far is dark-field lighting. The next step is to use conventional direct or reflector-diffuser lighting to top light the setup. Top and dark-field lighting are then carefully balanced for intensity. The final result will be to give an excellent view of all parts of the flower against a black background and with all the minute hairlike processes clearly shown. If color film is being used, substitute for the ringlight a pair of two mirror setups as advised for directional dark-field work (see Figure 17 and Plate V).

Herbarium sheets appear at first glance to be merely a variation of copy work, but there are complications. Herb sheets come in all types of relief, from dead flat to completely rounded. Generally speaking, the best way to show all the features is to light to very low contrast, to minimize shadows, and to emphasize color differences. This can be achieved by using carefully balanced reflector-diffuser lighting. If the more rounded subjects are to be shown for shape, and shadows would only serve to confuse, the best method would be to use a fluorescent ringlight around the camera lens. The light is essentially shadowless, but relief still shows well. Occasionally a more directional light may be desirable, and here the first method, with some degree of light versus reflector imbalance introduced, is used. In any case a sufficiently good background, if the print will show the edges of the herb sheet, is simply a white card laid directly under it.

It is normal practice to include a scale, usually metric, somewhere within the picture area to indicate sizes. Herbarium sheets are invariably delicate, and require very careful handling. *Do not flex the sheet* or the specimen may get cracked or broken. *Do not attempt to pin such a sheet to a wall* and photograph it with a horizontally mounted camera.

COPYING

A great deal of copying is done in conjunction with scientific research and, although there are standard references in the field (see Bibliography), some coverage here is desirable. Ordinary documentary copy can generally be handled most economically by the usually available commercial firms or by library copying services, but where more than normal care is required or it is otherwise necessary to do the work oneself it is necessary to have some knowledge of it. Photostating, reflex copy, and other such special processes will not be covered here; the following discussion treats only straight photographic copying. Before engaging in this work, however, the reader should refer to the available sources on copyright law (see Bibliography), violations of which can be embarrassing. Academic use of copyrighted material is by courtesy—it is not a right.

The standard lighting setup for copying is to have two lamps, one on each side of and equidistant from the original copy material, and each set at about a 45° angle to the optical axis. This results in an elliptical band of approximately evenly lit area. This area must be somewhat larger than the original copy, the size of the area being varied by adjusting lamp-subject distance (Figure 28).

For accurate reproduction it is essential to have the optical axis of the camera perpendicular to the copy surface. This perpendicularity can be attained in several ways: by measurement of the distances between all components, by measurement of the subject on the ground glass (an approximation practical only with large cameras), or by optical means (the Hasselblad camera company markets such an optical device). Except for engineering use and similarly exacting uses it is usually sufficient just to get close enough that measurement of the resulting photograph will reveal no gross irregularities.

The original copy material itself must of course be held as flat as possible. Where absolute flatness cannot be achieved, as with tightly bound books, or where the material has been folded and creased, such folds and gutters should be parallel to the lighting axis (see Figure 28). This will do away with any tendency to form shadows or highlight reflections at these points.

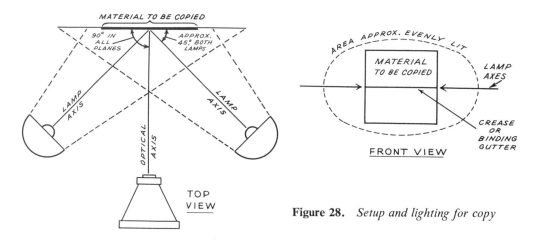

Figure 28. *Setup and lighting for copy*

Line copy is one of the most common sorts of copy. Line drawings such as the text figures in this handbook are examples of line copy. To produce negatives that will yield publication-grade prints or high-quality lantern slides it is necessary to pay close attention to the proper making of these original drawings. Fountain pen and pencil sketches are not worth troubling with. All lines should be a uniform true black, without breaks or weak gray areas. Even the commonly available drawing inks are sometimes not sufficiently dense, so one should obtain the special extra-dense inks which can readily be had for this purpose.

In many cases legends and labels are added to drawings in typescript. But it should be emphasized that only the very best typewriters (and typists) produce lettering even enough in density to reproduce well. Others will yield typescript which is uneven from one letter to another as well as among various parts of individual letters. Smudging and filling in of closed letters may also be present if the type is not clean.

The object of line copy is usually to produce prints or transparencies in which there is no "highlight" or "shadow" detail—that is, copy in which all lines are completely black and the background is pure white everywhere. This is most easily done with medium- to large-sized cameras through the use of "lith" type films. These are extremely high-contrast, thin-base films of great dimensional stability, usually orthochromatic in sensitivity (though panchromatic films of this type can be obtained), very slow in speed, and are primarily designed for and widely used in the printing industry. (The extreme high contrast, which makes the very black lines and pure white backgrounds possible, is also what makes the evenness of the original lines important.) These films have very high capabilities for resolution and provide excellent fine detail rendering and very sharp line edges. Ordinary photographic films have neither the contrast nor the resolution capabilities to give good results with line copy.

For 35-mm use there are available special, high-resolution films, now usually panchromatic, which can deliver either high or normal contrasts, depending upon the processing used. These films are also very low in speed— but copy doesn't move much. (Certain of these films can yield excellent high-resolution results in general photography if correctly used.)

In photographing inked line copy, particularly large sizes, a peculiar problem may enter. When examining the ground glass image or the finished print, parts of lines near the edges may appear as light or even white, instead of as the expected black. This is because of specular reflection on the ink surface itself, and arises where the paper surface is slightly rough and has produced a reflective inked surface at an angle sufficient to throw light into the lens. Slight bending of smooth papers may also produce this. Shifting the lights a little will usually correct this fault.

Continuous tone copy is any material which is not strictly line copy—photographs, half-tone reproductions, many etchings and engravings, and so on. In borderline cases it is necessary to very closely examine the original copy to be sure it is really one or the other. Material which superficially resembles line copy may upon close scrutiny reveal itself as continuous tone. This type of copy can also include such original materials as chromatograms, paintings, and other art works, and color slides, copies of which may be used for making black-and-white prints of them (this last will get special attention a little later).

If the original material is black-and-white and a reasonably accurate copy is desired, it is best to use one of the specially designed continuous tone copy films (Kodak's Gravure Copy film, available in sheet-film sizes, is an example). Exactly correct exposure and development are necessary for accurate reproduction.

If the original material is colored, a panchromatic film of normal capabilities should be used to render the relative brightnesses roughly as the eye sees them. Selective filtration here can also be used to emphasize some colors over others.

Copying in color is nearly always done to provide a projection slide where the original material is flat work not readily projectable. The main requirements of the film are reasonable accuracy in color reproduction and good contrast and resolution. Color copying can be done with either tungsten lighting or direct sunlight. Original paintings of large size can be readily copied by sunlight, which will ensure evenness of lighting. A good setup for making a sunlight copy is given in Figure 29, which shows a horizontal camera as seen from above. Working between 10 a.m. and 3 p.m. will avoid difficulties in color balance that arise from the sky coloring in early morning and late afternoon.

Surface reflections on paintings, either as an over-all haze or as a series of small glints, can be eliminated by the use of artificial lights, arranged for copy-

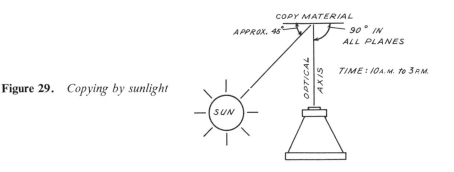

Figure 29. *Copying by sunlight*

ing and polarized as described on pages 55–56. Bright lights and wide diaphragm openings will shorten exposure times and obviate reciprocity failure, with its annoying color shifts. Polarizing filters are of little use when copying by sunlight, having no effect on over-all haze reflections but sometimes affording partial relief where a convoluted surface produces small reflections, some of which may be polarized to a degree.

Copying color transparencies as earlier noted, is sometimes desirable to provide a black-and-white print for publication, if the original photography was in color and reshooting the original subject is not practical. There are several methods.

Owners of 35-mm cameras may find that one of the several commercially available slide-copying arrangements can be used with their equipment. Inquiry of dealers will ascertain this, and instructions will be provided with the equipment. Properly used, these devices can yield quite satisfactory copies.

For those with other equipment there are two simple methods which can produce excellent results. The first is to place the color slide in the negative carrier of a photo enlarger, and project it upon a piece of panchromatic film placed on the easel, as in normal enlarging technique. The work must be done in total darkness to avoid fogging the film.

An easier method is to set up the equipment for diffuse transmitted light, as described in Lighting (p. 35). For best results use a black card, with a suitably sized hole, for a support. With the transparency placed over the hole and protected from top lighting, no light gets to the camera except through the slide being copied.

Copy negatives made from color transparencies commonly exhibit one notable trait. They are frequently, even usually, extremely high in contrast. To combat this, it should be standard practice to develop in very low-contrast developers. Printing may be simplified and improved through the use of divided development, which both lowers over-all contrast and slightly re-arranges those contrasts. (See Bibliography for references to low-contrast negative development and divided print development.)

For best-quality reproduction it is well to remember that the quality of the final result is limited by the quality of the original slide. Try, then, to use only slides that are sharp and clear and in which the lighting is suitable for print reproduction (see Plate XVI, A).

DISH CULTURES

Petri dish cultures appear at first a simple matter, with little likelihood of difficulty being offered the photographer, yet there is sufficient variety within the classification to require quite a range of techniques. Such cultures are of three general types: (1) fungus or bacterial colony cultures on and under the surface of the medium, (2) precipitation bands formed by interactions among substances within the medium, and (3) bacterial plaques and similar phenomena, which produce a clouded effect in or on the medium, comprising discrete circles of cloudiness on a clearer background or a completely clouded background with circles of relative clarity scattered here and there.

A problem likely to be encountered in any photography of a dish culture comes from the nature of the dishes themselves. Most glass petri dishes have concentric rings of uneven thickness in their bottoms. They may also have scratches, abrasions, and other physical malformations. This is countered by floating the dishes in mineral oil during photography. Several large drops of oil placed on the glass support is sufficient to just float the usual petri dish. Care must be taken to avoid having bubbles of air form in the oil beneath the dish, as these will be highly visible. Large bubbles indicate the need for a drop or two more of oil. A large number of small ones indicate prior turbulence in the oil. Handle it so as to reduce turbulence to a minimum. Application with a large pipette is preferable to pouring or the use of a bulb-type dropper. Glass dishes are preferred over plastic ones, even though the plastic ones have flatter bottoms. Plastic dishes frequently exhibit, when carefully viewed, minute radial internal cracks in their bottoms; although they do not affect the use of the dish, they show up glaringly in dark-field lighting. Oiling will not cure this defect.

Colony cultures are usually photographed by normal top lighting, either direct or diffuse (though occasionally interior detail may require transmitted light either solely or in combination with top light). The desired emphasis in lighting may be either on color patterning or surface relief, or both. If emphasis is on color, use evenly balanced reflector-diffuser lighting, and check the need for color filtration. If color bands are in shades of the same color, the lighting must be especially even, as high-contrast developing and printing will be needed. And this will render any unevenness of light highly visible.

Where surface texture or shape is the main point of interest, a more direct light is called for, with a single lamp being placed at a high angle (about 60° above the subject plane) to shorten and minimize the shadow of the forward edge of the dish. A white card reflector is then used on the opposite side to fill shadows and provide contrasts as desired. For shape alone the contrast can be quite high, but when color is also important the shadows should be well filled with reflected light in such a manner that while the shapes are clearly outlined the over-all contrast is relatively low.

Backgrounds can be either black or white, according to need and tastes. A white background provides a modicum of transmitted light, which is sometimes useful in showing some structures within the medium; but where it is necessary to show surface detail only, without confusion with such features, it is best to use black.

Precipitation bands within a culture medium can be shown by two methods. The culture can be desiccated and stained, and then photographed with diffuse transmitted light, or it can be photographed directly by using dark-field lighting, using either a fluorescent ringlight below (see Figure 17) or the mirror technique, producing directional dark field (as in Figure 18). The latter is particularly useful where the bands to be shown all face the same way. If the bands face in various directions, only an all around dark-field effect, such as the ringlight produces, will be able to show them all equally well. Either dark-field method will show the lesser and more inconspicuous traces more easily and clearly than will desiccating and staining.

Unfortunately, the dark-field methods will show dust, lint, and undissolved culture medium as well as or better than the precipitation bands. Great care, including rigorous attention to preparing and filtering the medium to be used, is necessary if one is to avoid spending long periods retouching such features off a print intended for reproduction. It is virtually certain that a few such extraneous materials will be present to show as white marks on the final prints. These, if the presentation is to appear competent, must be retouched out. Even though they may be inert and sterile in the culture, their visible presence is disturbing in the print.

Plaques show either as cloudy areas on a clearer background or as clear areas on a cloudier background. Once in a while the best solution is dark-field lighting, but usually the best result is obtained with diffuse transmitted light. Only observation of the individual plate will tell which should be used.

FOSSILS

Fossils usually occur either as stony objects or as more or less pigmented inclusions within a transparent medium (such as insects in amber). The methods of lighting fossils are various, depending upon what is visible and what is to be shown.

Stony fossils are of several general types. Some are free-standing objects, such as chunks of fossilized wood, bones, and shells, and are treated much like any other three-dimensional object. Generally, they are shown best with fairly diffuse lighting against—in most cases—a white background. If they are unusually light in color, then black makes the better background.

Other fossils exist as relief impressions upon a split-open stony matrix. These are best lit with a single flood or spotlight, placed to strike across the subject surface at a relatively low, grazing angle, the exact angle depending upon the degree of relief; it can be adjusted according to need and taste. If relief is exceptionally low and flat, no reflector is used, but ordinarily reflectors can be used to throw fill light into any shadowed areas to reveal the detail within them. In some cases a number of relatively small reflectors may need to be arranged carefully around the specimen to throw small amounts of light into specific areas. Some experimentation and ingenuity will be required to photograph a difficult specimen well. A curved specimen, for instance, may need to be lit as one would a cylinder. Orientation of lamp and subject must, of course, be one that will provide lighting generally from the direction of what will be the picture top, if the effect of reversal of relief is to be avoided (see Plate III, B).

A third type of stony fossil exists only as a stain on a rock face. Here the lighting must be flat, even and as nondirectional as possible, with little or no evidence of highlight and shadow. Lighting is by well-balanced reflector and diffuser (see Plate III, A). Color filtering may help. In some cases immersion in water will improve contrasts (see Plate IX, C and D). Before trying this, however, check the possibility that the subject is water-soluble. If water is used, it should be distilled water, to cut down the likelihood of bubbles. Some bubbling will probably occur through the emergence of air trapped within the specimen, but this is a temporary problem. Before an exposure is made, any bubbles present can be removed by gentle brushing with a watercolor brush.

Carbonaceous or other highly reflective deposits on or in a stony matrix make up a fourth category of fossils. They can be photographed by reflection principles with axial or near-axial lighting. The final print will then show them as highly detailed bright objects against a darker background (even though the original may be seen as coal-black against a light tan stone). If retention of color is necessary, they can be lit as the rock stain just discussed, but there may be less visible detail this way. Occasionally immersion in water may help here, although it is useless with axial-type lighting.

Amber inclusions. Insects and various other types of living matter are often trapped and fossilized in amber. When the amber has been selected, cut, and polished it is often photographed to aid in examining and recording the included matter. The subjects are usually quite small. The methods used for photographing them are—except for the matter of dealing with the amber itself—the same as for any other small object of similar aspect (see sections on Magnifications, p. 37, and on Insect Materials, p. 96).

The main problem in working with amber inclusions is the existence of both distortions resulting from uneven shapes and tilted surfaces and reflections from those surfaces. Fortunately the method for avoiding both these problems is the same. Prior to photography the amber is immersed in mineral oil, which has an index of refraction similar enough to that of the amber to eliminate both the reflections and the refractions. The presence of the oil makes for messy working conditions (and this oil must be kept off the camera and all its accessories), but the results are worth the mess. The use of the oil does introduce one unusual problem. Paper used for reflectors and diffusers will be rendered translucent by the oil and will not act as desired in controlling the light. It is desirable to make such reflectors out of white celluloid or other material that will not be affected by oil immersion. The diffusers can usually be placed outside the dish, so that no contact is made with the oil.

GEOLOGICAL SPECIMENS

Geological specimens in the round can be treated like the stony fossils (p. 92). In terms of lighting and photography they are similar.

An exception to this is the thin sections normally intended for photography through the microscope. We will not here discuss photomicrography as such, but useful information can often be had by photographing these at low magnifications by one of two methods.

For simple gross appearance, use diffuse transmitted light. (The results are quite good, though not as ultimate in quality as with photomicrographic lighting by the Kohler system.) For showing directionally oriented fibrous structure use the mirror system described earlier to achieve a directional dark field. (And the Kohler photomicrography will *not* do this.) In either case, polarization can be achieved if desired by placing a sheet of polarizing material somewhat below the specimen and putting a polarizing filter on the camera lens. Both setups are shown in Figure 30. A horizontal camera setup could be used, but the vertical system is more common and more convenient (see Plate IV, B and C).

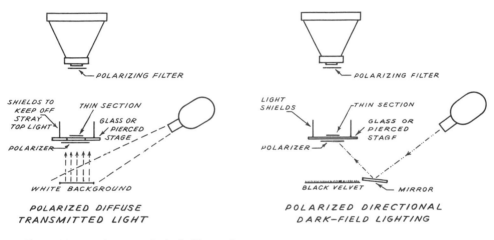

Figure 30. *Lighting geological thin sections*

IMPRESSIONS AND CASTS

Impressions are generally a relatively simple photographic task. Light should be grazing, to indicate relief. With small specimens the technique is the same as for relief fossils. Where the impressions are large, as with "squeezes" of cut-stone inscriptions, the lamp is placed relatively far away, to minimize a falloff of light across the subject, and no attempt is made to reflect light back across it, since to do so would lower the relief contrasts. Equalization of tones across the picture is accomplished in final printing. Use of grazing direct sunlight may be convenient, and if used there will be no falloff of light.

About the only question remaining is whether the final picture is to appear as one of the impression itself, or is to appear to resemble the original subject matter (as with inscriptions, which must be readable). In the first instance, used particularly where the original material itself is a cast or impression and the object making it has long since disintegrated, the impression is lit as is usual from somewhere generally at picture top. If the photograph must resemble the original inscription rather than its impression, the impression is placed— as is normal with any impression—with the side bearing the sharp imprint of the original subject facing the camera. The lighting is then arranged so that it comes from picture *bottom*, usually bottom right. If the negative is then printed reversed, the inscription will be readable and the relief will appear depressed rather than raised, as was the actual impression. Since the impression is itself actually a reversal of the original subject's relief, this apparent re-reversal will roughly recreate the relief of the original subject.

Casts, being more completely rounded out or even fully three-dimensional, are approached much as any other fully shaped subject. For example, dental casts, when upper and lower jaw impressions have been taken and have been placed together on an articulator, are photographed as follows.

Two lights are placed so their beams cross the face of the subject. This provides a grazing light along both sides, so that the shapes of the teeth are clearly shown. These lights must be carefully positioned, so that lighting as seen from the camera position will be evenly distributed. These lights can be either direct or diffused, according to the circumstances.

At this point, a special problem arises. With such dental casts, one of the primary objectives is to show the existence, sizes, and positions of gaps between opposing and adjoining teeth. With the above lighting arrangement these gaps will be submerged in the general shadows about the teeth. To show them clearly, special steps must be taken.

First, the background should be a piece of deep-nap black velvet. Then the space between the casts, representing the interior of the patient's mouth, must have placed within it some wisps of fiber-glass or cotton fluff. This material must be only just sufficient in quantity or it will block light rather than scatter it. Now a spotlight is directed into this fluff-filled space from the rear and slightly to one side. Light from this source will be scattered and refracted by the fluff in such a manner as to fill the mouth space with a general glow. When seen from the camera position, any dull-looking area is an indication of a thickening in the fluff, which should be picked out looser. Finally, cards are so placed as to keep the spotlight beam from touching any part of the casts except the interior space (see Figure 31). Correctly done, the final print shows the casts in shades of light gray against a black background, and with the gaps between the teeth (and them only) as clearly defined pure white areas.

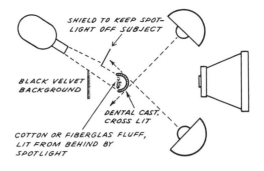

Figure 31. *Lighting dental casts*

INSECT MATERIALS

Most of the technical knowledge required for the successful photography of small objects in general has been presented earlier. But insects, being particularly small and unusually complex in structure, require some specialized comment.

As is usually the case, lighting presents the greatest single difficulty, once the general procedure of working at magnifications is understood. The greatest trouble comes from the sheer small size of the subjects. They are just too small in many cases to see just how the light is falling upon them. The solution, as with all really *small* objects, is to observe through a dissecting microscope while varying the lighting until the desired effect is obtained. Then the specimen is placed under the camera, and the lighting arrangement is carefully duplicated. After checking the results at the ground glass and correcting as necessary, the exposure is calculated and the picture made.

Some writers feel that the only ethical way to photograph any insect is in the wild, with no studio work or manipulation of the subject allowed. This is certainly the case where the normal living habits of the insects are of primary importance (and the Bibliography contains an excellent reference in this area). But where the insect being studied is extremely small, or where the important subject is not the normal habits and stance but rather the detailed structure of the insect, then field work becomes much less practical and studio work is both imperative and entirely correct. This latter approach will be emphasized here, and lighting suggestions for particular types of materials follow (see Plates XIV, XV, and XVI; Plates II, III, VII, and IX also show insect materials).

Insect eggs seem a good subject for beginning the discussion. Such eggs are in many cases white or very light in color. Photography in natural locations—on leaves, bark, other insects, and so on—is common, but if they have been isolated the background should be black. The egg is laid directly upon a piece of black velvet or on a piece of glass just above it. Dark eggs in isolation are, of course, done better against white.

Lighting depends upon circumstances. If the egg is textured and of a matte surface, lighting is by normal reflector-diffuser method, with the fixtures reduced in size proportionally. Reticulated surfaces, either matte or shiny, can be lit by a grazing light to emphasize relief, particularly if the egg is of the relatively common flattened "fried egg" configuration (Plate XIV, A). Eggs on stalks, such as lacewing eggs, are best shown in profile against a black background, with lighting arranged to emphasize edge boundaries and to show the stalk (see Plates VII, C, and XVI, A and F).

A special problem is found with eggs that have a highly polished surface and yet with an inconspicuous honeycomb pattern on them, a not unusual appearance. Diffused lighting does not show the pattern well, so the egg is lit with two direct lamps, one at each end (or one direct lamp and a small mirror simulating a second one). The effect will be to provide a definite highlight from each lamp, and within those highlights the pattern will show clearly. While the pattern will not show as clearly elsewhere, the lights can be so placed that one can infer the pattern's existence all over the rest of the egg.

With all such egg materials, and indeed all insect materials, the subject must be protected from overheating by placing a water cell before the lamp.

Pupae can be roughly divided into two general classifications: those which are opaque and dark, and those which are white or light and somewhat translucent.

The dark type are treated with normal reflector-diffuser or direct light-reflector lighting, according to the need, and are photographed against a white background if in isolation. There are seldom any great difficulties here.

The white or translucent pupae are, if isolated, photographed against black velvet. Usually the best lighting is provided by a single direct lamp about 45° above the subject plane and from the head end. Filling of shadows is effected by a white card reflector opposite the lamp. The harsh highlights caused by damp or shiny surfaces are eliminated by placing a polarizing screen in front of the lamp and a polarizing filter at the camera lens. Rotate one of them while observing the ground glass image, and fix it in position when the reflections disappear (see Plate XIV, C).

Protection from the heat of the lamps is necessary. Extreme heat will damage pupae, and even gentle warming may initially stimulate them to movement. Many pupae become active if disturbed, also, and may flop around wildly. If left a minute or so under the lighting to be used they will usually quiet down, however, and exposures running even to 20 to 30 seconds can be made without sacrifice of sharpness.

Larvae are in general handled much like pupae, although they are more likely to move about. They are most easily photographed in their natural surroundings, where if left undisturbed for a short time they will normally stop to feed. Even when crawling around there are often periods of several seconds in which they are quite motionless, and there will be time to focus and make the picture (Plates XIV, B, and XV, B). Occasionally it may be desirable to anesthetize a specimen which is either uncompromisingly active or insistent on burrowing into its surroundings (Plate III, D). If desired, of course, any movement can be stopped by resorting to flash, the only difficulties being those normal in close-up flash use (see earlier sections on Flash, pp. 27 and 46, sample situation in the Appendix, and Plate XVI, B–E).

Beetles. Because of the complexity of their structure and the multiplicity of their types, beetles are a photographically important breed of insect. Two features of greatest interest to researchers are the general structure and the pattern of coloration. Showing color patterns alone is sometimes aided by the use of color filters. Suitable lighting for showing both features simultaneously consists of a slight modification of normal reflector-diffuser lighting.

A single lamp (most conveniently a spotlight or one of the more powerful microscope lamps), aimed at the head end of the beetle, is directed downward at an angle of 30–45°, and lights both the insect and a white background below its support. The diffuser can be plain white tissue paper or, if more direction-ality of lighting is desired, a piece of translucent matte celluloid. The latter diffuses the light somewhat less than the tissue. This lighting takes good care of the whole frontal section of the beetle, but one problem remains.

Nearly all beetles have wing cases that round off at the tail end, roughly as a more or less flattened quarter-section of a sphere. Using a simple white card reflector to fill in at this end will produce an unrealistically light, crescent-shaped reflection on this portion of the wing cases. The way to avoid this, at the same time providing soft, even light to reveal fully the sculpturing and wing-case coloration, is to mask the lower part of the reflector with a piece of black paper that extends up to a level just above the center line of the beetle (just as is done for spherical objects, but in this case on one side only).

Some beetles have another characteristic which is tough to deal with. The wing cases, instead of having a gently curved cross section as is usual, are strongly curved and meet at the center in a sharply depressed groove. Almost any form of lighting results in longitudinal highlights and shadows which look in black-and-white much like color striping. (In color the effect is also present, but by virtue of the nature of color is less likely to be visually ambiguous.)

A method for at least lessening the problem, and sometimes completely doing away with it, is to reverse and modify the normal lighting scheme.

Place the lamp at a rather low angle at the tail end of the beetle and the reflector at the head end. Use no diffuser, but place a neutral density-filter—whose *only* effect, we have already seen, is that of lessening light intensity—before the lamp in such a way that the insect is shaded by it while the background and the reflector both receive the direct and undiminished light of the lamp. The strength of the neutral-density filter must be such that the diffuse light reflected from the card at the insect's head is slightly stronger than the direct light from the other direction; the reflector should be relatively low and wide.

The result, then, is this. The head end is lit by diffuse reflected light, the wing cases by a rather low-angled direct light. The appearance of normal relief is maintained by having the stronger light from the head end. The ambiguity of wing-case coloration is at least lessened and may be removed by the direct light up the groove. (This method is a variation of lighting for cylindrical objects, as discussed earlier.)

Shiny black beetles and other similar subjects present another special problem in lighting. Since most of these beetles have relatively undetailed wing cases but have considerable sculpturing about the head area, the lighting that gives the most natural appearance is a single high, direct lamp placed at the head end. No reflector is used, as it would only make unnatural-appearing reflections on the tail end of the wing cases. If this system is correctly used, the result will be to provide excellent delineation of the frontal sculpturing and a natural appearance of the wing cases—that is, very dark with small bright highlights to indicate shininess.

A second method is sometimes used here, where less realism is necessary but where maximum allover surface sculpturing must be clearly shown. Here a "light tent" surrounds the insect with a cone of diffuser material that is lit from all around evenly. This provides omnidirectional ultrasoft lighting and an effect of over-all highlighting. That is, the whole insect will appear rather light in color, with sculptural details as dark lines on it. There will be relatively little impression of glossiness.

Beetles are shown in Plates III, VII, IX, and XIV.

Transparent-winged insects also can present real problems in lighting. If the body of the insect is at all dark, it is difficult adequately to show both it and the transparent wings in the same black-and-white print (the problem is slightly less but still present in color). A good method, where over-all appearance is to be shown, is to use a dark background, light the body to emphasize edge delineation, and see that a light plays on the wings at such an angle that the reflection will cause them to show their patterning to the camera. In color light-tenting the insect against a medium-toned background can give good results.

Photograph pinned insects with spread-out wings with reflector-diffuser lighting and white background. Black out the background on the negative with opaque to increase contrast of wings and background, and in printing expose the body for less time than the wings to even out appearances.

Pinned insects present two problems, both associated with the presence of the pin. First, the pinhead, in dorsal views, may obscure important detail (see Plate VII, B). The solution is either to place the pin correctly originally or, where it is too late for this, to cut the pin off carefully just above the place where it emerges from the insect's body.

The second difficulty is presented when the lighting throws the shadow of the pin across the background. This can be avoided quite simply. A piece of medium-weight celluloid is used as a support for the subject instead of the usual glass plate. The pin is inserted into a hole previously made for it, and the background is placed at a little distance below the celluloid. A handy way of holding the celluloid stiffly is to cut it to fit one of the plastic snap-together frames which are made for holding $3\frac{1}{4} \times 4$-inch film slides for projection (Polaroid #633 slide mounts do nicely). The whole assembly can then be set across two blocks of wood above the white card background. The background, as is usually the case with three-dimensional subjects, should not be too large, or it will cause edge reflections on the subject.

Insects in amber have been discussed in the section on Fossils (p. 93).

Moths and butterflies are generally quite simple to photograph. They are usually photographed as mounted specimens with their wings spread out to show coloring. Lighting is low-contrast reflector-diffuser lighting, intended to emphasize wing coloration. With black-and-white films, selective color filtering may help. With color films, the lighting remains the same, but of course there is no color filtering except for correction of color balance.

Insect galleries in wood can be photographed in such a way as to portray best the galleries themselves and to show the sculpturing produced by the insect's mouth parts, or they can be photographed primarily to show their contents. The intended result dictates the lighting to be used.

In the first case it is most useful to light with a single direct lamp, angled according to the height of the relief and aimed across the general line of the galleries at about a 45° angle. Exact adjustment depends entirely upon the individual subject and upon the final effect desired. A white card reflector is used opposite the lamp to adjust contrast and partially fill shadows. It is most properly placed parallel to the line of galleries rather than at 90° to the light path, as is usual. This placement keeps the amount of shadow fill roughly constant along the length of the specimen. Properly done, the effect is to provide a good amount of detail on all flat or near-flat surfaces, a shadow next to one wall of the gallery, and a highlight illuminating the other wall (see Plate XV, A).

Where the insect is the point of interest and the gallery serves as its container, the lighting must be different—usually much lower in contrast. In most cases a good result is obtained by using reflector-diffuser lighting adjusted to give a soft, nearly directionless light; such directionality as remains should come from approximately picture top. This affords good general detailing and usually adequate lighting of moderate cavities and their contents. If the cavity is unusually deep and the insect is deep within it, then axial or near-axial lighting will be needed to achieve the necessary penetration and delineation of the subject (see Plate III, E). Axial lighting is also helpful in showing insect eggs that have been partially embedded in the floors and walls of galleries. Although it is not penetration of a cavity that is usually sought in this case, the eggs will be shown much more prominently because they will reflect more axial light than the rougher and less shiny wood.

Silk deposits, being made up of extremely fine strands of material, can be quite difficult to portray unless certain special steps are taken. Spider webs and other primarily radial silk structures can be lightly sprayed with a very fine mist of water, causing tiny droplets to form all over the web. With two lights placed one on each side, much as for copying, each drop will be clearly edge-lit, and the aggregate effect is a clear delineation of the entire web pattern.

Most worms that spin silk produce relatively amorphous masses of fibers, lacking the fine patterns of web spiders. Careful examination of these massed strands will, however, usually show a preponderant general direction of deposit. A good practice here is to use a single direct light at 90° to this line of deposit, with a reflector opposite to fill shadows in the whole area of the picture. Each strand which is so lit will appear as a discrete fine line of light in the picture, due to internal refraction (see Plate XV, B).

Leaf and needle miners, once the top surface of the mined leaf or needle has been peeled back to expose the occupant, can be photographed quite normally. And if you wish to show the external appearance of the mined leaf or needle, the best methods are those normal for any such botanical subjects (see Plate III, C). But if it is required to show the larva actually at work within the leaf, something else is required.

A shadowgraph or silhouette effect is usually the most appropriate means of doing this. Some subjects are shown best by using a strong transmitted light. Others, particularly needle miners, may show best when a directional dark-field lighting method is used. In this case, the mined needle should be placed at 90° to the beam of light reflected up from the mirror. (See Figure 17, p. 36 for details of the setup.)

Tiny active adults are a real trial of the photographer's patience. Magnifications of ×10 or more may easily be required simply to show general form, stance, and habits. (Detailed structure may only be visible in photomicrographs made of killed and mounted specimens.) Such high magnifications severely limit the depth of field, absorb light, restrict the field of view to an area substantially smaller than the usual area of the subject's activity, and magnify the insect's apparent speed of motion.

The most practical method is to prefocus the camera at a point very slightly above the surface of a clearly understood area; when the subject passes across this area, make a picture using a high-speed electronic flash lamp to stop the motion—a flash duration of at least 1/1000th of a second may be required if all parts of the insect are to be sharp. Light falloff, due to the magnification and its accompanying extension of the camera bellows, will often require the use of an accessory lens to concentrate the light beam. And the subject must be protected from the heat of the flash with a water cell. Experimentation may be needed to determine correct exposure. (See earlier section on Flash, p. 27, and look under Lighting, p. 25, and Magnifications, p. 46; see also Appendix.) Much patience will be needed in waiting for the insect to do what is wanted of him, and somewhere within the area depicted on the film. Therefore, the larger the film size, the better your chances (see Plate XVI, B, C, D, E, and G).

PORTRAITS

It may seem strange to include a section on portraiture in a handbook on scientific photography, until one remembers that scientific research is done by scientists. And most scientists are at one time or another asked to provide pictures of themselves for publication with articles or reviews, on book jackets, or for publicity use in connection with meetings, lectures, and so on. The general run of studio portraiture often seems rather unsuited to these purposes. The most commonly used substitute is a more or less bad snapshot made by some well-meaning but photographically handicapped associate. Hence this section.

No attempt will be made to enter into the intricacies of advanced portrait lighting, which can be quite involved technically. Nor will there be any effort to provide standardized lighting setups for the use of artificial light. The approach will be that of showing how existing light can be used to good advantage to provide what is in essence a glorified snapshot, an informal and relaxed portrait aimed simply at showing the sitter as he is, and without artifice. (An example of such informal portraiture is Plate XVII.)

For this purpose the preferred source of light for achieving good results with great simplicity is diffuse window light. Pleasant appearance can be gained by having the subject sit in a chair about 4–5 feet from the window and turned at about a 30–60° angle to it. The camera is placed roughly parallel to the surface of the window. The background can be simply a piece of black velvet (no shadow problems, good isolation of the subject), or it may be composed of out-of-focus elements of the subject's natural working surroundings. Filling of shadows on the side opposite the window is accomplished by hanging up a white card (or a sheet of newspaper or even a white lab coat), and adjusting it for distance to provide the degree of fill desired. For best results—good sharpness, reasonable depth of field, and minimum grain—I prefer very fast films in rather large cameras. (A sample situation might include a 4 × 5 or 5 × 7 camera, Kodak Royal-X Pan film of ASA 1600 speed, and normal development of about 5 minutes in DK-50 developer.) The result can be a really satisfactory portrayal of the sitter, with a degree of relaxation and intimacy often not obtainable in the circumstances of the studio. Quite satisfactory results can be obtained even with 35-mm cameras if a firm camera support is used, and again quite fast films (such as Kodak Tri-X Pan or Ansco Super Hypan).

Where artificial light is necessary, as in cases where the subject is to be shown surrounded by his laboratory equipment, one can still use only that light which normally occurs where the work is to be done. Most laboratories these days are lighted at quite a satisfactorily high level. The subject is moved about until a good lighting situation prevails, and then the picture is made. Again, firm camera supports will assist in gaining sharp pictures.

The most natural and relaxed appearance will occur if the subject sits or stands in a comfortable, normal position and with his features in repose. The subject may or may not be looking at the camera, but in any case the plane of principal focus should be at the eye nearest the camera. If the eye is in focus, all else can be out of focus and the effect can still be good. If the eye is out of focus, there is an irretrievable loss. Photographically speaking, the eye is the seat of the intellect and the window of the soul, the natural center of interest in almost any face. The only likely exception might be with a subject who is blind, in whom the best point of focus may be the lips or even the hands and gesturing fingertips.

TUBES

Test tubes and other tubular glassware are frequently the subject of photography for research purposes. Since they present several different types of problems, this section will be divided accordingly.

Tube slants, cultures in which the actual subject matter is plant material growing on the face of a slanting layer of culture medium, require special treatment for best results. Lighting is direct and undiffused, and comes always from the top of the tube (plugs must be so placed and height of lamp so arranged that no shadow falls on the actual subject). Light from the bottom of the tube or tubes would not only misrepresent the usually occuring surface relief, but would also make disturbing reflections on the curved end of the tube. No reflector is used, as it too would reflect on the tube bottoms (see Plate XVIII).

Backgrounds can be either black or white. If they are to be pure white in the final print it will usually be necessary to opaque the background on the negative, but with tubes this is not usually an arduous task, as the edges are simple in shape and easy to follow. A black background can be provided by laying the tubes directly on a piece of black velvet. Where backgrounds are black, tubes laid in groups will tend to reflect one another disturbingly, so dividers of black paper cut to a width slightly less than the diameter of the tubes are placed between the pairs. This setup will give a final picture in which the tubes are very inconspicuous compared to the setup with white background, and the appearance will be much as though the cultures had been removed from the tubes entirely and just laid side by side.

All growing cultures in closed glass containers will present the problem of condensation of moisture on the inner glass surfaces. To combat this, gently warm the tubes by waving an electric coil above the tubes until condensation just disappears. Use care, as overheating will damage the cultures. (When in doubt, test a typical culture for heat resistance before attempting this method.) The setup must be complete before heating is attempted, as the picture must be made before condensation returns (see Figure 32 for setup details; see

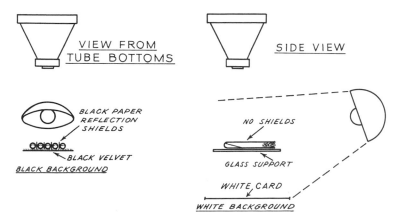

Figure 32. *Lighting tube slants*

Removing Bona Fide Artifacts, p. 57, for opaquing information and condensation removal).

Liquids in tubes or colored bands suspended in liquids or in transparent gels in tubes are a fairly common photographic subject. The usual best result will come through using a lighted white card behind the tube as a diffuse source for transmitted light, with no frontal light on the tube at all. Either color or black-and-white films can be used with this setup. There will be no reflections on the tube itself to take attention away from the contents.

If the white background is too small or too far away the edges of the tubes may be outlined by broad dark bands. The background should be adjusted in size and distance until there is only a thin dark border to indicate tube size and shape.

Precipitation bands in gel cultures contained in tubes are handled much the same as in dish cultures. A dark field effect, directional in this case, is obtained by placing a single light above and behind the tube and at a 90° angle to the band direction—that is, shining along the tube length (see Figure 33 for setup details).

Figure 33. *Lighting precipitation bands in tube preparations*

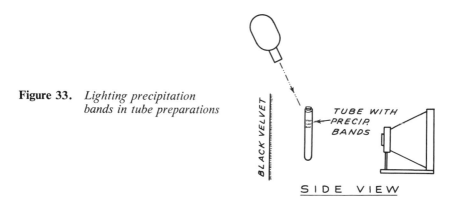

BLACK VELVET

TUBE WITH
←PRECIP
BANDS

SIDE VIEW

In this case, as in others where the background is black, the edges of the tube can be made visible by putting a piece of white card at each side of it, and adjusting their positions until a very narrow white reflection is seen all along both sides of the tube. In some cases a very good effect can be obtained by using a fluorescent ring behind the tube or tubes, as with petri dishes. There will be no necessity for edge cards here, as the tubes will naturally be edged with a very narrow band of white light reflected from the ring light.

Objects in tubes. Photographing three-dimensional objects cased within tubes can sometimes be trying, but in most cases it is readily handled by lighting with diffuse light from above and in front of the tube (see Figure 26,

p. 80). A reflector opposite the lamp usually serves only to confuse the issue by introducing unwanted reflections on the tube. Backgrounds are used as earlier described for objects in glassware: with black backgrounds, white cards at the sides produce light tube outlines; with white backgrounds, black cards produce dark outlines. With white backgrounds it may prove desirable to opaque the background on the negative so that it will print pure white and thereby differentiate from the glass tube better.

If the subject matter within the tube requires a more complex type of lighting, it is sometimes practical to immerse part or all of the container in water, thereby killing the reflections on the glass surface. With test tubes that are not sealed, an aquarium can be used, with the tube held at its top by a lab clamp and as much of the tube submerged as may be needed. The glass side of the aquarium on the side toward the camera should be of good quality plate, and the camera axis should be at 90° to it, to assure best optical conditions. A sealed container, such as an electronic vacuum tube in which the important subject matter is the inner workings, can be placed in a tray of water below a vertical camera, and kept submerged with a sheet of glass laid over it (itself under the water surface). Lighting the container's contents can, in either case, then be approached in the normal fashion.

ZOOLOGICAL SUBJECTS

The multiplicity of possible zoological subjects precludes detailed discussion. Photography of wild fauna in the open will not be described, as it is well covered elsewhere (see Bibliography). Bones and other such objects are treated photographically about like any other three-dimensional object. Comment here will be limited to the following three examples.

Bird skins are most commonly photographed in small groups, to show comparative patterning. This is very well accomplished by laying the skins in the proper order directly on a white card. A fluorescent ringlight (or, more suitably, a three-ring fluorescent fixture as described earlier) is mounted so as to surround the lens of the camera and thereby produce near-axial lighting of the subjects arrayed below. The soft nondirectional light obtained by this method is well suited for the job and gives exceptionally fine detailing of feather color and structures. The background will normally print either pure white or so close to it that it will serve as such.

Living animals to be photographed in the studio can be photographically troublesome. A simple side wiew is the usual pose desired, for the purpose of showing clearly the form, coloration, stance, and any deformations or other pathological conditions. Elephants, camels, and other large mammals can be simply photographed outdoors, so we will limit discussions to the smaller creatures.

The most suitable lighting arrangement will probably be that described earlier for potted plants (see Figure 27), using a curved white card (or, with very light-colored subjects, a similarly placed piece of black velvet) for a background, and well-diffused lights. Here, however, the lamps used should most conveniently be electronic flash, in order to stop movement and obtain a picture at the precise correct instant.

In order to produce the most informationally useful picture, the negative should be fairly well filled by the subject. With animals that are likely to move around much, this is best done by measuring the subject beforehand and arranging the camera so that the field of view covered is of suitable size. A wood block or other dummy subject is then placed correctly and the camera is focused on it. The final preparatory step is to place marks on the background material to indicate both the edge limits of the picture area and the principal plane of focus. When the setup is ready, the focusing block is removed, the correct exposure determined, and the lens diaphragm and shutter are set (see Figure 34 for details).

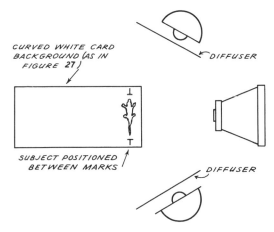

Figure 34. *Setup and lighting for photographing live animals in the studio*

At this time the animal is placed on the background between the positioning marks and with its longitudinal axis along the principal plane of focus. Care should be taken, of course, to alarm it as little as possible while doing all this. Many animals will, when set down, immediately set out to move forward and explore their surroundings. If it is set down a couple of inches to one side of the desired position, you can get your hand out of the picture area just about in time to make the flash exposure while the animal is passing through the marked area (see Plate XIX).

Visceral preparations and other views of animal interiors are best photographed using a vertically mounted camera, and with direct lighting from the head end or one side with reflector fill opposite. A polarizing screen before the light and a polarizing filter at the lens, as described earlier, will make it possible to eliminate nearly all the disturbing reflections which are normally present in this type of subject matter (see Plate XX). Cutting out these reflections by immersing the subject in liquid is usually practical only with such things as single complete organs which have been dissected out. Backgrounds, if they show at all in the picture area, should usually be white. Small animals pinned to boards for dissection will present a good appearance if a piece of white card is placed on the board prior to pinning. Any shadows thrown on this background card will be rendered very light by the reflector fill, and will not appear disturbing (see again Plate XX).

INTRODUCTION TO THE PLATES

Pictures in the following plates are of three types: (1) they have been made as part of the daily operations of the University of California's Scientific Photographic Laboratory, (2) they were made as deliberate examples of things discussed in the text, or (3) they are pre-existing examples of the author's personal photographic interests. Most are in the first category.

Where they are the product of Laboratory operations, the permission of the owner was obtained and the credit line "Originally photographed for ————" is affixed. Where persons contributed subject specimens to be used for making illustrations, the credit line used is "Specimen provided by ————". The portrait of Dr. Northrop and the coin owned by Mr. Gans were done independently of the Laboratory. All uncredited pictures except the lacewing series were done to illustrate points in the text. The lacewing series is a project of personal interest that fitted in well here.

All photographs are by the author and any technical deficiencies can thus be clearly assigned.

Readers should again be reminded that, although the subject matter of a given picture may be foreign to their field, the characteristics being shown and the principles involved in photographing them may well apply to their own needs. Thus, for instance, the heavy emphasis on insect materials in the accompanying plates is due both to the easy availability of suitable specimens and—more importantly—the inherently great variety of such materials; the characteristics displayed in many of these insect photographs may also be readily seen in other, vastly different types of subject matter.

In describing the plates, just as in the text in general, technical terminology (such as "petiole" or "labial palps") is kept to a minimum in order to allow maximum ease in understanding matters for readers attempting to draw conclusions from pictured materials outside their own field.

PLATE I | *Printing Levels and Contrasts*

Mineral specimen ($\times 2$)
Lighting is with one direct flood lamp from the upper right, with minor reflective fill opposite. White card directly below subject. No extra light used because of darkness of subject.

A. Too low in contrast, with printing time adjusted to give good highlights. General effect is "muddy."

B. Correct contrast and printing level. Highlight areas (the small light inclusions) just show slight detail; the shadows do the same.

C. Too high in contrast. Printing time adjusted to show good shadow detail, highlights "washed out."

D. Too high in contrast. Printing time adjusted to show good highlights, but shadow areas go dead black.

C. and **D.** Note that while each shows some areas well, neither is a good over-all print.

A

B

C

D

PLATE II *Isolating The Subject*

A. and **B.** Crystalline edge on a mineral specimen ($\times 2$) is revealed by casting a shadow on the area below and behind the main interest edge.

C. Needle miner damage ($\times 3\frac{1}{2}$), shown to best advantage by color filtering. A medium red filter darkens the green needles and thereby increases visual contrast between the needles proper and the yellowed mined areas. [Originally photographed for R. W. Stark and J. N. Borden.]

D. Beetle larva ($\times 20$). Mouth parts isolated by differential focus. Background, the insect's own body, is out of focus while the mouth parts are shown sharp and clear against it. [Originally photographed for H. V. Daly.]

Black velvet used for each background.

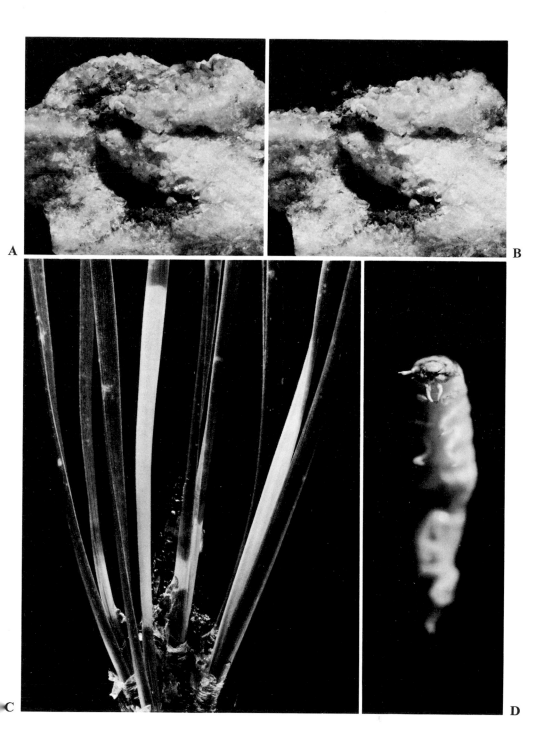

A

B

C

D

PLATE **III**

Basic Lighting Methods I

A. Fossil shell (×2) light tented to show color only, very little impression of relief.

B. Same subject lit with reflector-diffuser lighting adjusted for relatively high contrast in order to emphasize surface texture.

C. Mined leaf (×1) lit by a single direct flood-lamp from direction of leaf tip to best show relief. Color filtering increases contrast between mine and leaf proper.

D. Breech block of .380 automatic pistol (×2). Breech is closed, and all light is provided by a beam-splitter, throwing light directly down the gun barrel. Note excellent definition of machining marks on face of breech block. Axial lighting.

E. Beetle resting after emergence from pupal stage (×2). Dark subject lying at bottom of a deep cavity cannot be effectively lit by any means other than axial lighting from a beam-splitter. [Originally photographed for E. G. Linsley and Arthur Raske.]

Black velvet background in A, B, and D. In C, a white card is used, with extra lighting. In E, a white card is placed directly below subject and is lighted by same light as subject.

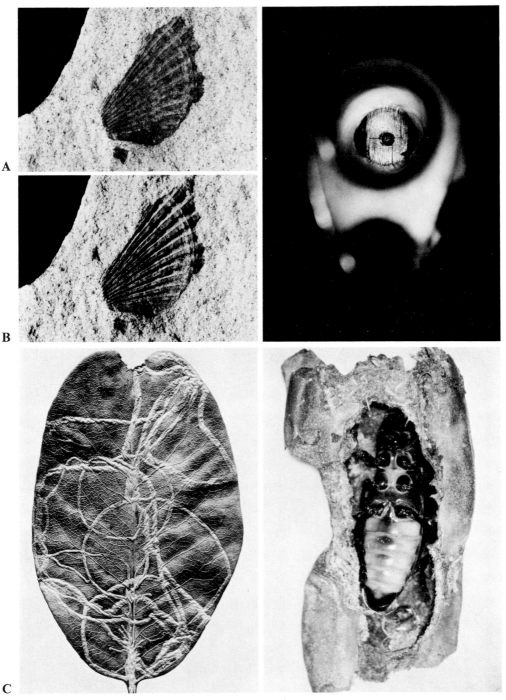

PLATE **IV** | *Basic Lighting Methods II*

A. Fish spine (×8) lit by diffuse transmitted light, no top light. [Originally photographed for Howard Bern and Kinji Yagi.]

B. Mineral thin section (×5) lit by diffuse transmitted light, no top light.

C. Same area of same subject, polarized diffuse transmitted light with crossed polarizers. [Specimen provided by L. E. Weiss.]

Each employs a white card below, with no top light but with standard diffuse transmitted light.

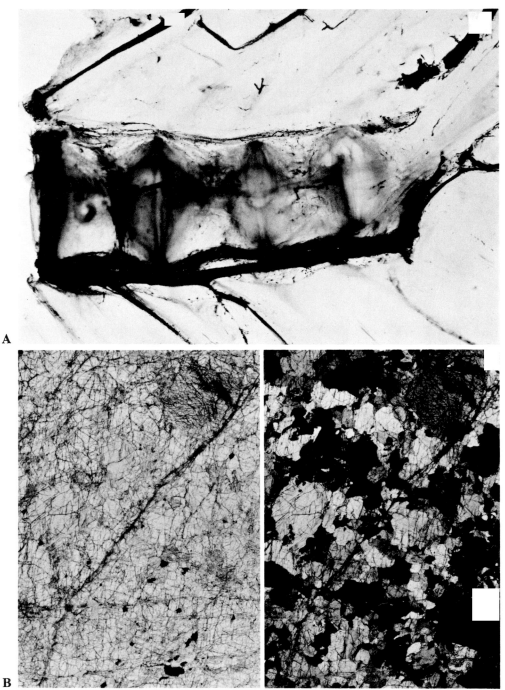

A

B

C

PLATE V | *Basic Lighting Methods III*

A. Dandelion seed head ($\times 2$), by ringlight dark-field lighting.

B. Same subject, same lighting, but with sole addition of one direct lamp beam providing frontal lighting from left side.

C. Dissected flower parts ($\times 2$) with ringlight dark-field lighting coupled with balanced intensity of direct floodlamp top lighting from direction of picture top, and reflector fill opposite. [Originally photographed for Lawrence R. Heckard.]

Black velvet background in each case.

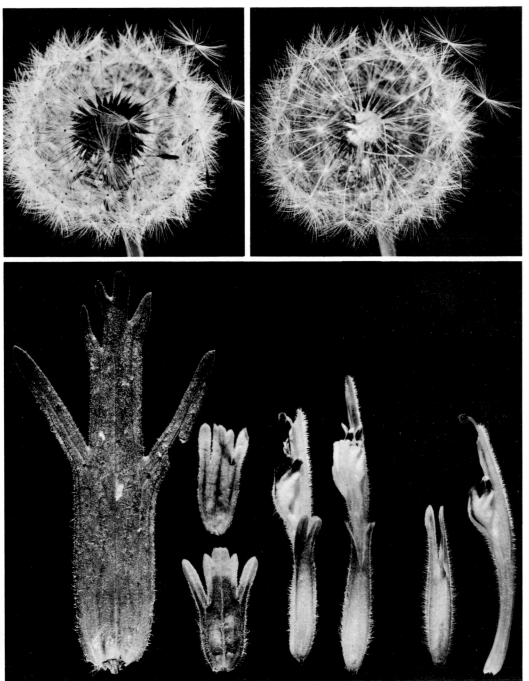

B

PLATE **VI** | *Filtration Effects*

A. Leaf ($\times 1\frac{1}{2}$) lit by direct light from tip end, reflector fill opposite. No filter, panchromatic film. A white card is used below, with usual extra light as described.

B. Same leaf, same lighting, same film, deep red filter.

C. Same leaf, same lighting, same film, deep green filter.

Note: See color plate, Plate VII, A, for actual color rendering of this same leaf.

A   B   C

PLATE VII | *Color Plate*

A. Leaf (about ×1), same subject as on Plate VI; use this picture to judge color filtration effects shown there. If possible, observe this color picture through various filters as described.

B. Longhorn beetle (×3.25), pinned specimen. Direct lighting from direction of head end, minor reflective fill opposite. This lighting is perfectly practical in color, particularly transparency color, but too contrasty for good black-and-white usage. [Specimen provided by John Chemsak.]

C. Lacewing egg (×15), direct lighting from right side to show (1) the stalk lit by internal refraction, and (2) the larva within the egg (the striped effect). If lit otherwise the latter would not show, the egg simply appearing light green all over. See Plate XVI for black-and-white copy of this same picture.

D. Grasses (about ×½), direct lighting from picture top, with no fill lighting. This is too high in contrast to transfer well to black-and-white. The maximum relief effect is good in transparency color.

All backgrounds, black velvet.

A

B

C

D

PLATE VIII | *Solutions to General Problems I*

Lighting Spheres and Cylinders

A. Spherical subject, immature plum ($\times 2$), illuminated reflector-diffuser lighting as in Figure 9. The lighting is poorly balanced; the background, too large. The latter results in severe edge reflections all around.

B. Same subject, lighting for spheres as in Figure 23. The lighting is much improved; the edge reflections, greatly decreased by use of a smaller background. If a background of the same shape as the subject were so sized and so placed as to provide only a narrow white border all around the subject, *all* edge reflections would disappear. The rest of the background could then be rendered white by blocking it out with opaque on the negative.

C. Cylindrical subject, a pin vise (about $\times 1$), lit by reflector-diffuser lighting with the lighting axis *across* the subject axis. The effect is quite dramatic, but tends to give such erroneous impressions as blending with the background on one side, a false appearance of striping in polished areas, and so on.

D. Same subject, identical lighting setup, but with lighting axis *along* the subject axis, with end lighting. It is less dramatic, but also less ambiguous. Which type of lighting should be used is dependent upon the effect desired in the particular case.

White card background below, lit 100% extra.

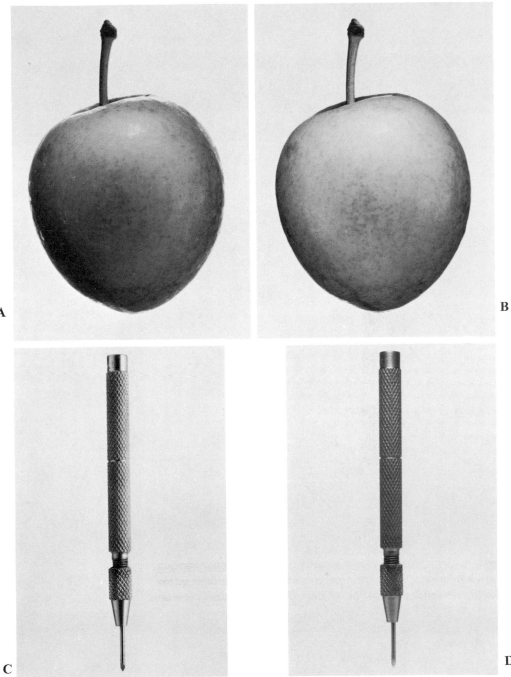

PLATE IX | *Solutions to General Problems II*

A. Longhorn beetle ($\times 5$), grazing direct light from picture top to show surface hairs, no fill, directional dark-field lighting with mirrors to show edge hairs. [Originally photographed for John Chemsak.]

B. Leaf ($\times 1\frac{1}{2}$), grazing direct light from picture top to show tiny hairlike processes all over leaf, reflector fill opposite.

C. Fossil ($\times 5$), reflector-diffuser lighting to emphasize color staining. Normal film and developing, printed to highest possible contrast. Note presence of dust and lint all over subject, left uncleaned as a demonstration.

D. Same subject, lighting, film, and developing. Over-all contrasts much improved by immersing subject in water during photography. No need for high-contrast printing. [Originally photographed for W. Berry.]

A and B, black velvet backgrounds.

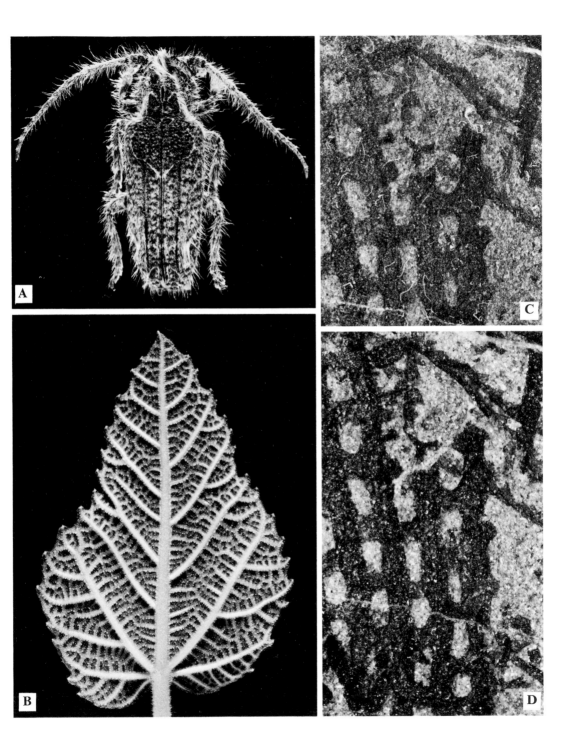

PLATE X

Apparatus on cat skull (about ×1). Over-all lighting provided by two diffused floodlamps, one on each side of the camera at about 45° off the optical axis. Detailing of the flat metal surface required a variation of lighting by reflectivity. A white card was hung vertically above the subject and slightly behind it. It was lowered during visual observation until from the camera position its reflections appeared on the polished flat surface, thereby lightening that entire surface in a fine soft manner. The card was lit by the same lights as the subject. Owing to the high polish of the flat surface, the use of a direct reflectivity lamp would have made too harsh an impression. [Originally photographed for O. T. Ellsworth.]

Background is a white card curved up behind. On the negative the background is blocked out with opaque to ensure whiteness.

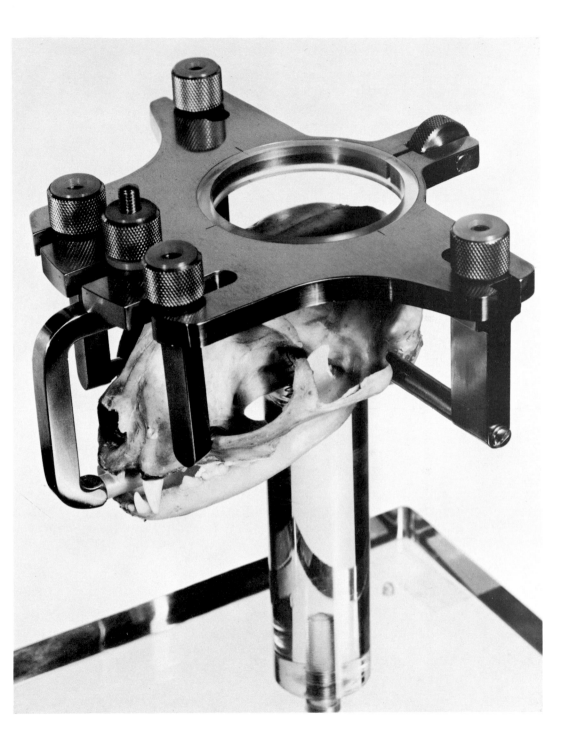

PLATE XI | *Art Objects and Artifacts I*

A. Antique coin ($\times 1$), lit near-axially by ring-light and with aluminum foil background as in Figure 6. [Originally photographed for Edward Gans.]

B. Chinese coin ($\times 1\frac{1}{2}$), lit axially by beam-splitter to best show extremely low relief.

C. California Indian stone bowls (substantially reduced in size), lit by multiple ringlight. This lighting provided (1) excellent cavity penetration, and (2) very good indication of the comparative amounts of relief present in the three specimens. The background was a plain white card directly under the bowls. No need for blocking out background as it prints white. [Originally photographed for Albert Elsasser.]

The backgrounds in A and B are aluminum foil, as described in the text. In C, a white card lit by the same ringlight as subject; the card appears very white in contrast to the darkness of the subject. In preparing the halftones used in printing, however, a white background becomes light gray (see Plate VIII): here the background was removed by the engraver, as noted on page 20.

B

C

A

PLATE XII | *Art Objects and Artifacts II*

A. Alaskan Eskimo mask ($7\frac{1}{4}$ inches high), Lowie Museum of Anthropology, University of California, Berkeley, catalogue number 2-5849.

B. Alaskan Eskimo mask ($9\frac{7}{8}$ inches high over faceboard), Lowie Museum, catalogue number 2-6926.

Note: Both masks were photographed using diffused flood lighting, one lamp on either side of the camera. The intention was to show both shape and coloration.

The backgrounds, black velvet.

A   B

PLATE XIII | *Art Objects III*

A. Sculpture by Charles Ashman, contemporary American. Over-all height of piece, 19 inches. Plaster over cardboard, painted. Lighting by existing window light only; subject and camera were moved about until desired effect was achieved. Background was 2 red cards for suitable gray shading.

B. Ceramic by a contemporary Italian (Caldognetto family, Milano). Head-to-foot length of child, $3\frac{7}{8}$ inches. Colored glazed ceramic. Lighting was by a single well-diffused flood lamp from far left, about 90° off the optical axis; no fill lighting at all. Black velvet background.

A

B

PLATE XIV | *Insect Materials I*

A. Grasshopper egg mass (×9). Direct flood-lighting from top right to show surface sculpturing on eggs. [Originally photographed for Woodrow W. Middlekauff.]

B. Larva on pine tip (×2). There is a frass deposit next to the larva, and at top center next to a bud is a silk deposit. Reflector-diffuser lighting, directed from picture top. [Originally photographed for R. E. Stevens.]

C. Translucent-type pupa (×4). Diffused light from picture top, no fill. Resulting shadows allow mouth parts to be clearly seen. Pupa had troublesome surface shines, which were completely removed by polarizing the light (a polarizer screen was placed inside the diffuser, a polarizing filter at the lens). Multiple tiny bright spots are surface sculpturing. [Originally photographed for John Chemsak.]

D. Longhorn beetle (×6). Preserved specimen, not pinned, relaxed and positioned to show desired features. Reflector-diffuser lighting modified as described in text for lighting beetles. [Originally photographed for John Chemsak.]

Backgrounds in A and D, a white card below, with extra light as usual. In B and C, black velvet.

PLATE XV | *Insect Materials II*

A. Insect galleries in wood ($\times 1\frac{1}{2}$). Direct flood lighting from top right with minor reflector fill parallel to left edge. The lighting is calculated to show both the galleries themselves and the "tool-marks" made by the insect on the floors. The background is a white card below, later opaqued on the negative. [Originally photographed for John Chemsak.]

B. Silk deposit on cone ($\times 5$). Direct lighting from top and slightly to left, reflector fill opposite. Direction of light roughly at right angles to that of main silk strands. Note presence of living larva just above silk deposit. The background, black velvet. [Originally photographed for R. W. Stark and J. N. Borden.]

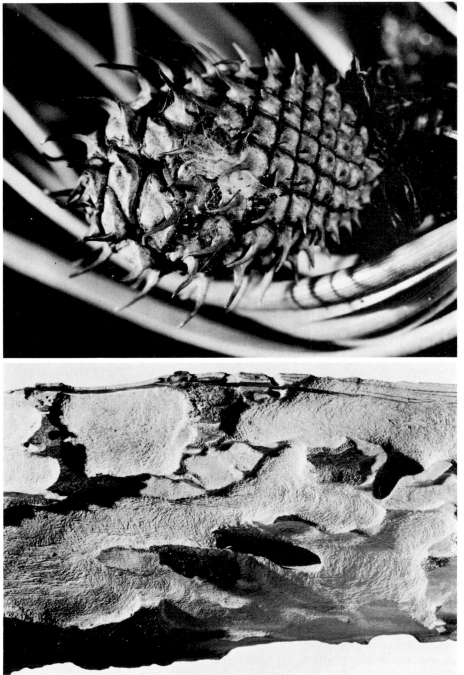

B

A

PLATE XVI

Insect Materials III

A to **F.** Series depicting a lacewing larva leaving its egg.

A. Lacewing egg (×15), showing stalk and evidence of the presence of the developing larva inside the egg (the striping effect). This picture is a copy of a Kodachrome slide. A color reproduction of it is on Plate VII, C.

B. Larva (×8), resting on egg case just after exit, body flexing constantly.

C. Larva (×8), climbing down stalk.

D. Larva (×8), on leaf walking away from egg stalk.

E. Larva (×8), dorsal view, walking.

F. Empty egg case (×15), lit and positioned to show exit rent. The stalk is not visible except across leaf at lower left, being out of focus.

Note: B to E are all by electronic flash as described in text. The pictures are contact prints of parts of 4 × 5 negatives made with a vertically mounted view camera.

G. Adult gnats (×8), both walking rapidly. Dorsal view is a male, side view is a female. Photographed with electronic flash as described in text. Real detail is practical with such small active insects only when natural movements are in some way almost entirely restricted. [Originally photographed for R. E. Doty.]

The backgrounds in A through F, black velvet. In G and H, a white card with the same light as subject. (If extra light were used, the card would be too white and wing detail would be lost.)

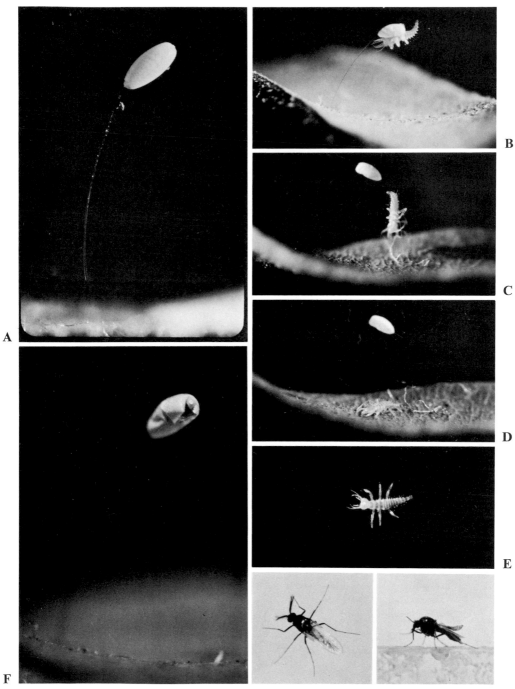

A

B

C

D

E

F

G   H

PLATE **XVII** | *Portraiture*

Laboratory portrait of Dr. John C. Northrop, winner of 1946 Nobel Prize in chemistry. Lighting was normal window light only, no fill light at all. Camera was an 8 × 10 view camera using 5 × 7 Kodak Royal-X Pan film (ASA 1600), developed normally, 5 minutes in DK-50 developer.

PLATE XVIII | *Tubes*

Tube slants of fungus cultures ($\times 1$), lit according to white background setup shown in Figure 32. The background was opaqued on the negative. Since in this case the background received the same light as the subject and the subject is light in color, it would have printed as a light gray if the negative had not been painted. [Originally photographed for Shirley Nash.]

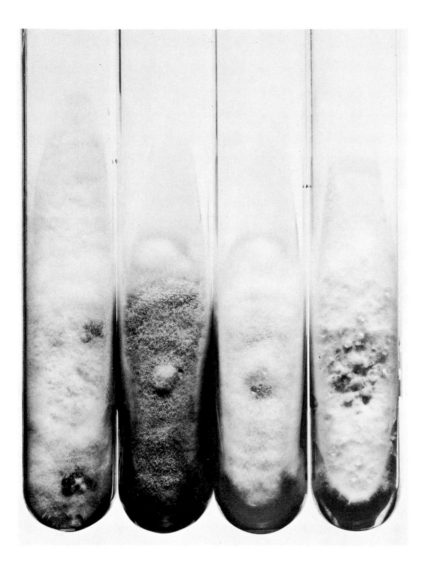

PLATE **XIX** | *Studio Photography of Living Animals*

A. Afflicted mouse ($\times$1), setup as in Figure 34, using a black velvet background. [Originally photographed for J. Fong and Isobel Contento.]

B. Cat with experimental apparatus attached to skull (substantially reduced). Setup as in Figures 27 and 34, with curved white card background. [Originally photographed for O. T. Ellsworth.]

Note: Both pictures were made using electronic flash lighting to stop motion.

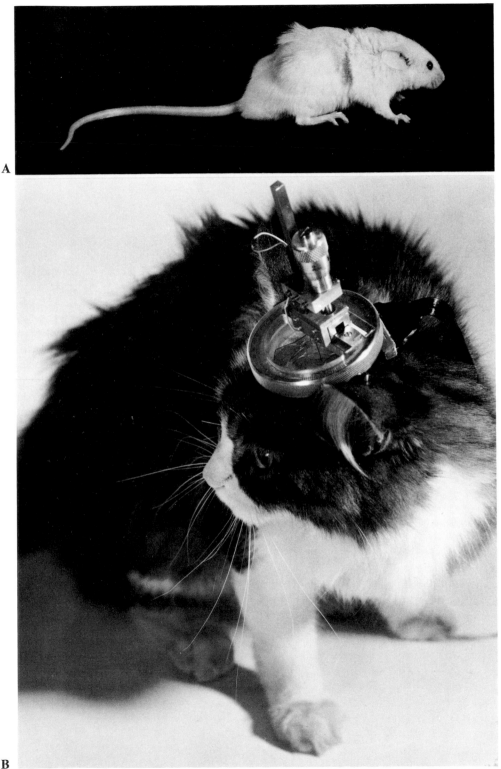

A

B

PLATE XX

Visceral Preparations

A. Mouse with tumor ($\times 2$), lit from top right with a single direct light and reflector fill opposite. Background is a white card, and mouse is pinned directly on it. Lighting is not polarized. Note reflections. [Specimen provided by Ben Gordon.]

B. Same subject, identical lighting. A sheet of polarizing material was placed in front of the light, and a polarizing filter was placed at the camera lens. When properly rotated with respect to one another these filters removed nearly all of the reflections, thus reducing ambiguities in the picture. The result is a picture which is less dramatic but which more truly portrays the subject.

Note: The tumor is at the lower right corner of both pictures.

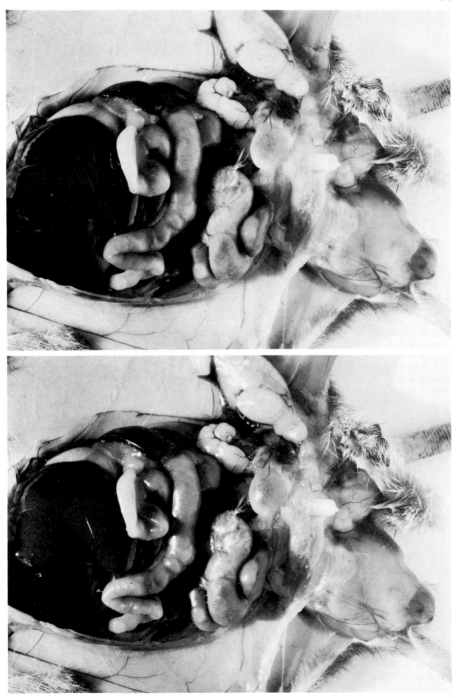

B

A

SAMPLE FLASH EXPOSURE GUIDE FOR CLOSEUPS

MAGNIFICATION	EFFECTIVE APERTURE LENS SET F/16	SUBJECT/BULB DISTANCE (IN INCHES)
1	32	44.4
2	48	30
3	64	21.6
4	80	18
5	96	15
6	112	13.2
7	128	11.2
8	134	10.8
9	150	9.6
10	166	8.8
11	182	7.9
12	198	7.2
13	214	6.7
14	230	6.2
15	246	5.9
16	262	5.5
17	278	5.2
18	294	4.8
19	310	4.6
20	326	4.3

The above table assumes the use of an Amplex PF-1 flash bulb in a 5-inch matte aluminum reflector, and film having with this bulb a guide number of 120 (such as Kodak Panatomic-X). Other films, bulbs, reflectors, and so on, will give other results.

TO CALCULATE TABLES SUCH AS ABOVE To find lamp-to-subject distance, knowing the f-stop to be used, divide guide number by effective f-stop number. Result is distance in feet and tenths of feet.

To obtain the correct guide number under these nonstandard conditions, start by assuming the manufacturers' guide numbers correct, and make such corrections as operations with your particular equipment suggest. At very close distances some reflectors are likely to throw a nonstandard pattern of light and thereby disturb the accuracy of the manufacturers' calculations.

BIBLIOGRAPHY

A detailed bibliography of all materials in this field would be very extensive and is outside the intent of this handbook. The sources listed here are chosen to give a representative selection of items considered particularly applicable to the fields discussed. Most of the sources listed contain more or less extensive bibliographies themselves, and thus further expand the available resources. The last item listed is a general bibliographical compendium of photographic sources in all areas.

The relatively heavy dependence upon the Eastman Kodak materials is not meant to imply any particular endorsement of that firm or its products, but it does reflect two facts. These booklets are very useful, and they are all quite readily obtainable almost anywhere.

Sources are grouped under the text heading deemed most appropriate, though it is obvious that many of them cover other areas equally well. Remarks are included to help clarify the contents of the entries.

REVIEW OF ESSENTIALS

Exposure Meters and Practical Exposure Control
J. F. DUNN Fountain Press, London

This book is not known to me personally, but is highly recommended by Mr. Ralph Steiner of New York, whose opinion I value.

Photo-Lab-Index
HENRY M. LESTER Morgan & Lester, New York

The standard technical encyclopedia, with quarterly supplements available for keeping up to date.

Photographic Lens Manual and Directory
C. B. NEBLETTE Morgan & Morgan, New York, 1959

Contains a good treatise on basic photographic optics.

Camera Techniques for Professional Photographers
EASTMAN KODAK BOOKLET

View camera operation.

Corrective Photography
LEWIS L. KELLSEY L. F. Deardorff, Chicago

View camera operation.

Processing Chemicals and Formulas
EASTMAN KODAK BOOKLET

Good general coverage of photo processing and formulas for all basic black-and-white chemicals for those who prefer to mix their own.

Negative Making for Professional Photographers
EASTMAN KODAK BOOKLET

The Negative
ANSEL ADAMS Morgan & Lester, New York, 1948

An excellent work by a great photographer.

Photo Methods for Industry, Jan., 1960, p. 46
"GRAIN," BY H. J. WELLS

The best explanation of this phenomenon that I know.

The Print
ANSEL ADAMS Morgan & Lester, New York, 1950

About the best available source on printing techniques.

U.S. Camera, June, 1962, p. 46
"Divided development," by PAUL R. FARBER

A useful supplemental printing formula and method. Particularly good with border-line negatives.

GENERAL TECHNIQUES

The Complete Book of Lighting
DON D. NIBBELINK Midland Publishers, Forest Park, Ill., 1950

A good survey of orthodox lighting.

Filters and Polascreens
EASTMAN KODAK BOOKLET

A good general survey.

Kodak Wratten Filters for Scientific and Technical Use
EASTMAN KODAK BOOKLET

Not a duplication of *Filters and Polascreens*, but a detailed survey for technical users.

The Theory of Optics
PAUL DRUDE Dover, New York, 1959

An inexpensive reprint of a classic text, translated from the original German. Old, but still useful.

Concepts of Classical Optics
JOHN STRONG Freeman, San Francisco, 1958

A more up-to-date work designed as a college text, well illustrated for help in understanding by laymen.

Color As Seen and Photographed
EASTMAN KODAK BOOKLET

An Introduction To Color
RALPH M. EVANS Wiley, New York, 1948

General coverage, broader and deeper than the source immediately above.

Eye, Film and Camera in Color Photography
RALPH M. EVANS Wiley, New York, 1959

The finest work on theoretical and psychological effects in photography I have yet seen. Not by any means limited to color work. A must for anyone seriously interested in photography.

Applied Lighting, Bulletin 0-241 Sylvania Lighting Products

"Color photography under fluorescent and mercury lighting"
Technical information for those who must do color photography under nonstandard lighting.

SOLUTIONS TO PROBLEMS, GENERAL AND SPECIFIC

Making Service Pictures for Industry
EASTMAN KODAK BOOKLET

Applicable to apparatus photography.

Photo Methods for Industry
A monthly periodical with occasional useful articles.

Journal of the Biological Photographic Association
A quarterly periodical.

Copying
EASTMAN KODAK BOOKLET

Legal Aspects of Photography
ROBERT V. SHERWIN Greenberg Publishers, New York, n.d.

Insects Close Up
EDWARD S. ROSS University of California Press, Berkeley, 1953

A good source on field photography of living insects.

Photography and the Law
GEORGE CHERNOFF and H. B. SARBIN American Photographic Book Publishing, New York, n.d.

This book and the one following can answer most general questions concerning copyright, libel, and so on.

The Veliger, Jan., 1961, Vol. 3, No. 1
"Basic Lighting for Shell Photography," by ALFRED A. BLAKER

Photographing Nature, A Handbook for the Beginner and the Expert
DAVID LINTON The Natural History Press, Garden City, New York, 1964

A widely generalized text on photography of living creatures, with emphasis on small camera work in the field—though not limited to that.

SUGGESTED SOURCES IN OTHER AREAS OF INTEREST

Infrared and Ultraviolet Photography
EASTMAN KODAK BOOKLET

Photography Through the Microscope
EASTMAN KODAK BOOKLET

Photomicrography of Metals
EASTMAN KODAK BOOKLET

Photomicrography In Theory and Practice
CHARLES P. SHILLABER Wiley, New York, 1949

A definitive work, laid out as a coherent academic course.

Photographic Reproduction of Slides and Film Strips
EASTMAN KODAK BOOKLET

Effective Lecture Slides
EASTMAN KODAK PAMPHLET

Single copies available free on request from Kodak. A very useful illustrated discussion on standards in slidemaking; explains what will and will not be practical for showing on the screen.

A Handbook of Biological Illustration
FRANCIS W. ZWEIFEL University of Chicago Press, Chicago, 1961

A paperback text for those who need to make charts, graphs, line drawings, and other nonphotographic illustrations.

Photographic Literature
ALBERT BONI Morgan & Morgan, New York, 1963

A bibliography of the whole field of photography.

INDEX